Exhale

Exhale

An Overview of Breathwork

Gunnel Minett

With a Foreword by
Jim Morningstar

First published in 2004 by Floris Books
© 2004 Gunnel Minett

British Library CIP Data available

ISBN 0-86315-464-6

Printed in Great Britain
by Biddles Ltd, Guildford

Contents

Foreword

On first reading Gunnel Minett's *Exhale: An Overview of Breathwork,* I was both excited and relieved. The excitement came from the beauty of seeing all the pieces of a giant jigsaw puzzle of healing traditions come together. The relief stemmed from her truly satisfying presentation of how the growing field of breathwork addresses many timely and pressing questions in our world today.

I believe this book is a significant step in publicly clarifying the meaning of breathwork and establishing it as a domain of knowledge and a healing art. To give meaning is to put into context, to draw relationships to already established knowledge. Gunnel traces the lineage and contextual background for the growing field of breathwork. She assembles the elements of breathwork's ancestry in both western and eastern cultures and gives us a cogent overview of the use of breathing techniques throughout human history. Thus, the story of the labour and delivery of the current breathwork movement is elegantly recorded.

Meaning is more than historical location, however. True meaning brings being to life. Gunnel breathes life into the concept of breathwork by guiding us from the microcosm of breath's molecular effects in our organism to the macrocosm of breath's opening to transpersonal archetypes. This is a thrilling journey that ushers us into the heart and mystery of our own birth and the continual rebirth of humanity. We bear witness to the birth of breathwork in the process. Attendant to the relief that comes with successful delivery of a new being, of course, is always the wonder of what it will be when it grows up. Here again Gunnel foreshadows breathwork's future.

Breathwork is born of ancient tradition and time honoured practices as well as contemporary discoveries and applications of psychology and healing arts. Gunnel gives us clues as to why this is so important in our present day. To heal and grow requires retaining what is essential to our core while transforming our mind and body to present reality. Breath is that thread of life which anchors us to unchanging principles of Truth, Simplicity and Love, while allowing us to adopt and create anew in an ever-changing environment. We have come to a place in our history when the differences between cultures and traditions impact humanity on a global scale. If we do not access what is common and mutually essential to our nature, we are in danger of letting our apparent differences destroy life as we know it on this earth. Breath is our common denominator. Breathwork is a holistic technique which has the breadth and depth to unite the warring parts of ourselves and our world. It is truly the prototypical healing modality for the evolving global community.

Gunnel, herself, helped the dawning of international cooperation when she hosted the first Global Inspiration Conference for breathworkers in 1994. This meeting opened the minds of breathworkers around the world to unite their visions. Just hearing of this concept of a collaboration among schools of breathwork was transforming to me. I had an established School of Spiritual Psychology and Breathwork Training Program since 1980. The invitation to immersion in global breath, nonetheless, seemed to more fully bring disparate parts of my 'greater self' together. The fact that this conference has continued every year since in a different country and that it has inspired the creation of the International Breathwork Foundation and the International Breathwork Training Alliance is a testimonial to its timeliness in our world.

The world is always in transition, however. What makes this particular time different than others, and why is breathwork so important this time? The major shift in global consciousness as I have followed the research over the past 25 years is from linear and causal thinking to systemic and holistic thinking. This has marked profound watersheds in all areas of human endeavour from science to politics. We literally are awakening and using parts of our brain that have not been heretofore employed. We are able to appreciate interactive effects rather than one-dimensional A causes B causes C. We are able to glean the untapped resources within us rather than postulate separation, isolation, lack and impoverishment as our birthright. We are able to experience the interconnectedness of the fabric of our being and utilize non-social energies that did not exist in Newtonian world models.

Breathwork is uniquely suited to advance a holistic worldview in that it affects and links all levels of our triune brain. It opens pathways to the brain stem by consciously altering the breath patterns and activating our most deeply entrenched survival programs. It taps the resources of the mid brain and accesses the wisdom of our limbic system while helping release suppressive and unnecessary inhibitory responses. It brings the neocortex on board by reorganizing thought processes that have continuously activated conflicting responses from our mammalian and reptilian systems. It links us to the 'greater self' by opening awareness to our non-ordinary links to the cosmos.

The philosophy of 'creative thought' behind rebirthing /breathwork has been a rudimentary bridge between linear and holistic thinking and as such has been often misunderstood. When breathwork takes us to levels of non-social awareness we experience the truth of our identity being merged with a larger context and purpose. Therefore what from our local perspective seems bad or tragic because it does not lead to a consensus reality version of happiness or harmony, can be experienced from a holistic perspective as part of a larger dance of life. The trouble is that we are in two places — or I should say one place and another non-place — at once and our communication can appear grossly incongruent. Chaos theory is another such bridge and helps us see further than our local experience of fear and pain e.g. 'How can the death of my child be reconciled with a benevolent universe?' As Paul Pearsall points out in *The Heart's Code*, when we speak from our head we are referencing the logical reality of linear time and causality; when we speak from the heart we are invoking an understanding beyond conventional reality in which love prevails, even in the face of apparent disaster.

When someone glibly invokes a universal principle, such as, 'everything is in perfect order,' because they are uncomfortable with the pain of someone's loss, it is their fear which is operating, not their compassion. Consequently this 'heady' interpretation of 'creative thought' is misused and hurtful.

Breathwork as a newly emerging field has attracted a wide spectrum of proponents, practitioners and critics. Perhaps compassion is in order even for those who in their process of change, clumsily use or even misuse the tools of understanding and healing. This is a learning process and involves experimentation. Without those who have the courage to break out of the old paradigms, our learning would not advance. Fortunately, there are those, like Gunnel, who have dedicated their loving intention and wisdom to culling out the essential truths and valid working principles to serve as standards along the way.

This is not a 'how to' manual of breathwork techniques. Gunnel gives enough introductory data and references to allow readers to follow up on their interests and intuitions with established schools and practitioners.

The accomplishments of this text are first of all to help reduce the stigma of the new knowledge and technique emerging from a holistic paradigm which runs counter to the common Western thought processes of the last two centuries. The present book, just as the 'breath' itself, bridges the traditions of the past with the healing potential of our newly emerging world. Secondly this work, I believe, will stimulate cooperative learning and research amongst various schools and traditions which have operated for their own survival in relative isolation. Finally, the most personal benefit for readers I hope will be to increase the level of understanding and open the doors of the heart to explore and discover the type of breathwork best suited as a vehicle for their own healing and growth.

In light and love,

Jim Morningstar, Ph.D.
Director, Transformations Incorporated
Coordinator, International Breathwork Training Alliance

Introduction

Fifteen years ago, when I started writing my first book about breathwork, I had to search hard for explanations as to what goes on in the body when we breathe in different ways. This time around it has been much easier: over the last decade there's been a phenomenal increase in research into alternative approaches both to health and to our general understanding of the universe. Even respectable scientists, who have lived most of their lives within the prevailing scientific paradigm, have suddenly decided they can no longer ignore evidence simply because it does not fit in with the established worldview. Many have abandoned their academic careers and — sometimes with the passion of religious missionaries — declared their new perspective. This has led to an abundance of well-written and well-researched books presenting fascinating insights into the functioning of the body, the human mind, consciousness and how everything in our universe is related, that turn conventional science on its head.

Despite all this, however, we still lack an explanation of the effect which optimal breathing has on the body and psyche. Characteristically, conventional medical research focuses on pathology — establishing what happens when things go wrong. Modern medicine prefers to concentrate exclusively on how illnesses occur and develop. This approach obviously makes medical diagnosis easier since it ignores the patient's habits, general outlook on life and personal history. But regardless of convenience and (short term) financial gain this approach does not present the full picture — important elements are being overlooked thus weakening the patient's chances of a full recovery.

Mainstream medicine's heavy focus on illness means that we know little about health and how healthy it is possible for us to be. Conventionally, ideas about what is possible in terms of health are based on statistics within current populations. Consequently, we know how well we are now — not how well we could be if we changed our lifestyle and environment. Nor do we know very much about exactly what we need to do to be healthier. What is missing is an understanding of the optimal functioning of our body and psyche. If we start from such a vision of optimal health, we can then work backwards to try to establish what we need to do to achieve it.

Despite its absolutely essential, as well as central, role for our wellbeing, very little direct research has been done on the power and effect of the breath. On the other hand, a lot of work has been done which, indirectly, indicates the effects which different ways of breathing can have, and we'll be taking a closer look at these. Evidence of these effects is appearing in many areas. New findings in biochemistry, in particular, are providing scientific confirmation of thousands of years of intuitive knowledge. Modern science is beginning to accept that body and mind are not separate after all, but rather interact so closely that it is impossible to separate them: science can now show that thoughts and emotion greatly influence bodily functions and that the body can have an equally great influence on thoughts and emotions — indicating that it is possible for a person to become healthier simply by re-evaluating their thoughts and emotions; that it is possible to evoke the body's innate ability for self-healing and that this is more effective the more emotionally positive we feel. But crucially for our purposes, science has shown that the way we breathe has a central role in all of this.

One of the key roles of a breath technique is its capacity to induce altered states of consciousness. For many people, experiencing such states leads to a search for deeper meanings in life. For some this may result in the deepening of an existing religious faith, while for others it may initiate a more open-ended spiritual quest. Still, regardless of individual circumstances, many people in the modern world feel a need for more 'scientific' explanations of such 'nonordinary' states of consciousness. But this, in turn, will probably require the transformation of what we commonly think of as 'science.' For this and other reasons, there's an increasingly urgent need for a paradigm shift in many academic disciplines. The philosophical and cultural framework that supports western science is finding it increasingly difficult to accommodate the empirical findings of this science: scientific progress is going to require an expansion of what is regarded as 'scientifically acceptable.' Contemporary physics has been leading the way. It is made clear that the conventional western worldview is too narrow to encompass a full picture of reality. The findings of the new physics simply don't make sense within conventional western conceptions of reality: there will either be an increasing accumulation of 'inexplicable' or 'supernatural' phenomena, or our overall worldview will have to change.

Some examples can illustrate the directions in which a transformed scientific worldview may take us. Firstly, in quantum physics it is now well established that a phenomenon can be both a particle and a wave at the same time. In modern psychology a similar 'duality' is developing in so far as human behaviour has both a biological and a psychological aspect. Human phenomena can be seen both as behavioural patterns and/or chemical reactions within the body — the one does not exclude the other. What's needed is a holistic view that can include many aspects of the same phenomenon. Secondly, the new worldview will almost certainly have a curious (or perhaps not so curious) resemblance to some of humankind's most ancient theories. Most of these ideas are of Asian origin, maybe because Asians have been more effective at preserving this ancient knowledge — India, China, Tibet and Japan all have unbroken traditions of direct teaching stretching back thousands of years. Such traditional knowledge is not unique to Asia but it is much more culturally accessible there than in other parts of the world and, if it is to be incorporated into a new scientific worldview, it will almost certainly come in via the Asian route.

What we can already see is that this ancient Asian wisdom appears to match the latest scientific evidence better than conventional western knowledge. Using these theories we can get plausible and very accurate explanations of newly discovered phenomena. The circle between ancient knowledge, religion and science is closing. Mystical explanations may no longer always remain esoteric: they are becoming both widely accepted and scientifically verifiable.

The intention in this book is to highlight the role the breath has in our lives. It is also to describe the latent power and capacity which can be generated by conscious breathing techniques, regardless of which 'school' or method of breathwork is employed. Clearly, breathing has an utterly central role in our lives — we can't exist without it, so perhaps even to limit the role of the breath to various breathwork techniques is to take too narrow a view. But in order to structure this book, I've divided breathwork techniques into old and new. My intention is not to present a complete list of all techniques available — and indeed many that are presented are not examined in any systematic or exhaustive way — but rather to examine the phenomenon of breathwork as a whole, in all its myriad aspects.

Neither is it my intention to focus on breathwork as a psychotherapeutic tool, despite the fact that the psychological aspect of breathwork has a somewhat central role throughout this book. The explanation for this is simply that breathwork's psychotherapeutic role has been predominant in its emergence into modern western society. There's nothing to indicate that this will remain the same in the future. More and more people who come into contact with breathwork through psychotherapy continue to use it as a tool for their personal and spiritual development. If, following its long period of materialistic development, the western world is to reclaim the ancient knowledge which the East has preserved, then breathwork may have a key role in this process of recovery and integration. And under such a new scientific paradigm, breathwork will almost certainly have an important role in the medical practice of the future.

The book is divided into four chapters dealing with different aspects of the breath. The first chapter is an overview of the impact that the way we breathe has on our body and soul. It also puts the breath into a wider socio-cultural context. We look at how central the breath has been to human life for thousands of year and note the anomaly of the modern western view that reduces it to a mere physical function.

In Chapter 2 we look more closely at the potential power in the breath and consider how it is possible to consciously change the breathing pattern in order to achieve positive changes — both physically and psychologically. We look at old and new breathwork techniques, some in more detail than others.

Despite the common view that psychological problems are a form of malfunction, we will see that they are perfectly normal functions, designed to protect us. We will look at how the slow development of the brain demands a supportive environment for the child and how disturbances can cause psychological problems. We also look at how the experience of birth plays an important role in our lives and how disturbance during birth can give lifelong problems.

The breath is also, of course, a major influence on our inner lives and we examine the deeper psychological aspects of breathing. Despite claims of originality from the western breathwork schools, which have developed breathing techniques mainly for psychotherapy, we will see that they do not, in fact, differ greatly from the ancient techniques. Nor are these schools very far from the mainstream of western psychological development. On the contrary they are clearly rooted in this strand of modern psychology.

However, since breathwork falls between established categories for healing the body and psyche, it does introduce a whole new approach to psychotherapy. It is no coincidence that the Latin words for breathing and spirit have the same

origin: the spiritual dimension of breathwork has been recognized for thousands of years. We also examine how
breathwork can be used as a method for accessing the
'higher self.' And we consider transpersonal experiences,
which often arise from breathwork experiences. As the
name implies, these experiences provide deep insights that
go beyond the personal history of the individual to the ultimate nature of reality and the wider concerns of all human
kind.

In Chapter 3 we examine the physiological aspects of
breathing: how we breathe and what happens in the body
when we breathe. We also look at the role of the breath as
an aspect of the body's natural healing power. In order to
understand how the breath influences the body and mind,
we consider some basic brain functions and how they influence our psyche and capacity for self-healing. To clarify the
link between physical and psychological healing, we turn to
traditional eastern medicine where the breath has a much
more central role than in the West and to modern psychological explanations. We look, briefly, at how modern western medicine came to under-value the healing power of
breath and speculate as to some possible routes for its future
development.

To complete our overview of the power and capacity of
the breath, in Chapter 4 we consider the future of breathwork. What is the potential role for breathwork? Will it
become an alternative to the methods of physical and psychological health-care that are conventionally practised
today? There are many indications in this direction.
However, breathwork is still widely regarded with the same
suspicion and scepticism that generally attaches to 'New Age'
ideas. So, we conclude by examining what New Age actually
stands for, how 'new' it really is and what its future may be.

A major problem in presenting an experiential technique
like breathwork in a book is that merely reading about it is
never going to provide complete knowledge of it. It has to
be personally experienced to be fully appreciated. I've tried

to meet this need in two ways: firstly, the book contains some basic breathwork exercises and, secondly, it has a Resource List appended with information for those who want to go further and seek the help of a professional in order to have a deeper experience of breathwork.

Finally, a mild word of caution: the breathing exercises described in this book are designed to give a first taste of the power and capacity of our breath. Beginners can try them safely without special knowledge or further instruction. But even simple and short exercises can, potentially, have a deep impact on the body. It is important to remember that breathwork takes one into a subtle world where even a small movement can have a great impact. The purpose of these breathwork exercises is to achieve a positive result. It is therefore important to pay full attention to how your body and mind are reacting during the exercises; let your intuition guide your inner journey. It is a powerful protective force, which if listened to carefully will never take us further than the level with which we are comfortable. Your intuition knows what is best for you. If it tells you to find an expert before you try any of the exercises, then do so! Remember that the breath is your best friend and, as with all true friends, it should be shown both respect and trust.

Be inspired!

1. The Importance of the Breath

And the Lord God formed man
of the dust of the ground
and breathed into his nostrils
the breath of life;
and man became a living soul.

Genesis 2:7

The role of the breath

In all cultures and throughout history breathing has been regarded as the most vital of human bodily functions. We can survive without food and water, without being able to move or think. But without air to breathe we can only survive for a few minutes. We reckon our lives from the first breath to the last, and, despite the life-preserving miracles of modern medicine, it is still the spontaneous act of breathing that determines if a person is dead or alive.

The volume of air we breathe in every day is approximately five times larger than the volume of food and drink we consume. On average a normal, healthy person breathes 12 to 14 times per minute. During one year this amounts to more than 7 million breaths. If we live to be 80 years old we will breathe around 600 million times. Despite this few of us know much about the connection between how we breathe and our general wellbeing — apart from the fact that it is essential that we keep breathing, minute after minute, hour after hour, day and night in order for us to continue our existence on this planet.

So why do we pay so little attention to this essential and central bodily function? One probable explanation is the modern western conception of physical and psychological wellbeing: when we feel well we take it more or less for granted without enquiring much about what is affecting what. Not until the body starts to malfunction do we start searching for causes and effects, and even then the search is usually conducted within a very narrow conceptual space. Generally, little attention is paid to the wider connections between various bodily functions, despite the fact that recent research is revealing how closely all the functions of our body are linked together. Most people understand that we breathe less when we are stressed but few have ever tried to find out why and what effects it may have if we deliberately change our breathing pattern.

This lack of interest can probably be linked with western medicine's very limited interest in the bodily function of the breath: breathing provides the body with its vital supply of oxygen — and that is, basically, all it does. As so often in western medical research, breathing receives attention only when its normal functioning is disturbed in some way. And even this, in the case of the breath, is quite new — the study of the effects of poor breathing is a relatively new discipline. Given the vital importance of breathing, it is still not getting the medical attention it deserves. However, we are learning more about the effects of poor breathing and a number of symptoms have been identified and rightly linked with poor breathing. One example: it is now accepted that otherwise healthy people who do not breathe sufficiently may develop hypertension — a chronic state of increased tension in the body's muscles — a condition that can cause a wide range of problems such as high blood pressure, obesity and depression.

But we still have a long way to go before we fully understand — and know how to use — the positive potential of the breath to improve our psychological and physiological wellbeing. Westerners need to realize that much more is going on when we breathe than just delivering oxygen to the body. The traditional cultures have long known that the breath is also the best way to access our inner world — we can reach deep into our psyche and transcend our physical boundaries simply by changing the way we breathe.

In cultures that recognize the full potential of the breath, its many beneficial effects are usually assigned to three distinct areas:

—A physiological and spiritual cleansing process that can help us to explore and influence the mind.
—A healing power that can be used for medical purposes and to trace the origin of illness.
—A religious or spiritual path that brings us in touch with other dimensions.

As mentioned above, we know that poor breathing leads to ill health, but, of course, the reverse is also true. Using the breath to heal both body and psyche is one of the oldest forms of medical practice, dating back to prehistoric times and occurring in all cultures.

In prehistoric cultures, medical functions were generally carried out by medicine men and shamans. They were also responsible for maintaining positive relations with the spirit world so that the tribe could live in peace and harmony with themselves and their environment. They did this mainly by putting themselves into trance states where, in various ways, they could communicate with the spirit world and get strength and information from a higher world than their own. One way to achieve the trance state was by deliberately altering their breathing pattern. In some cultures, other tribal members also participated in breathing exercises. They often consisted of rhythmical dances or monotonous movements or chanting, which induce a specific breathing pattern. In several parts of the world these traditions have survived, and here breath has maintained a central role and importance.

A holistic approach to healing is fundamentally linked with the concept of 'making whole': to heal someone requires a grasp of the 'whole picture' when evaluating the factors that have led to the illness. Apart from mapping the development of the illness and prescribing the correct medical treatment, this should also involve investigating the thoughts and emotions which may be influencing the patient's body chemistry. Mobilizing both body and mind in the healing process makes the chances of recovery very much greater.

Another 'non-western' aspect of the healing process is acceptance: sometimes it does not help to try to control and fight the course of an illness. Instead it may be more effective to try to find a deeper meaning as to what is happening to a person's body. This can be sought through inner experience, where a person can examine himself or herself without judging, analysing or criticizing and as a consequence find peace and mental clarity. Real change in the course of the disease may require such inner work on a level deep enough to generate a permanent healing effect.

The goal is not always to get rid of negative emotions as quickly as possible. Sometimes it can be more important to realize that what has taken years to build up inside us is deeply rooted and there for a reason. And in order to get rid of negative emotions we may need to express them. We may need to find ways to express the thoughts and words behind an emotion before we are ready to let go of it. Part of this process may also involve changing the perception of ourselves and the world we live in. Breathwork plays an important role in all of this.

The link between breath and spirit is equally strong: the potential of the breath to access our inner world has been known since prehistoric times and in the broad span of human history, it is only really western culture in recent centuries which has ignored and forgotten this aspect of the breath. Other cultures, particularly China, Japan, India and Tibet, have kept the spiritual tradition of the breath alive. An exciting recent development has been the rediscovery of this connection by modern science: quite independently and clearly from a completely different philosophical perspective, it has come to the same conclusion — that the breath has a central role in our physical and psychological wellbeing. One of the purposes of this book is to try to re-integrate some of the lost ancient knowledge into the western world and to synthesize this wisdom with modern research on breath and breathing. As we will see, a key word in this enterprise is balance: without balance there is no harmony and without harmony nature does not function as it should, and the same is true for us. It is important to stress that the aim here is a synthesis of ancient wisdom and modern research. I shall, therefore, try to avoid seeing them as antagonistic camps, one of which is destined to predominate over the other.

> *The most important result of the practice of anapa-sati*
> *or 'mindfulness with regard to breathing,'*
> *is the realization that the process of breathing*
> *is the connecting link between conscious and subconscious,*
> *gross-material and fine-material,*
> *volitional and non-volitional functions,*
> *and therefore the most perfect expression of the nature of all*
> *   life.*
>   Lama Anagarika Govinda

Natural breathing

Despite the general western neglect of the breath, most of us do have some awareness of our breathing, if only in a negative sense. When, over the years, I've discussed, in various contexts, the importance of how we breathe, I have often heard the comment; 'I know I don't breathe properly.' But when I've asked what 'proper breathing' means few have ventured any ideas and none with any certainty. So let's start from the beginning and look at how we 'ought' to breathe — our natural breathing pattern. Alexander Lowen gives the following explanation:

Natural breathing — that is, the way a child or animal breathes — involves the whole body. Not every part is actively engaged, but every part is affected to a greater or lesser degree by respiratory waves that traverse the body. When we breathe in, the wave starts deep in the abdominal cavity and flows up to the heart. When we breathe out, the wave moves from head to feet.[1]

So there is a natural way of breathing, to which all healthy children are predisposed at birth. When we breathe naturally the body receives all the oxygen it needs to function optimally. Our natural breathing also relaxes the body so that the circulation functions well and supplies the various parts of our body with sufficient energy.

Breathing is different from our other body functions in many respects. For example, it is both automatic and can be consciously controlled by the will: we don't need to continually remember to breathe, however, we can alter our breathing pattern whenever we wish. The fact that we can influence our breathing pattern gives us endless flexibility both on the physical and mental level. Since the body requires so much less oxygen at rest than during physical exercise, it is essential that the breathing is flexible. If not we would never be able to put physical pressure on the body. The normal breathing pattern would simply not be enough to sustain the body during physical exercise. On the other hand, if we engaged in 'physical exercise breathing' all the time we would never be able to relax. It would be like driving a car without gears — either straining the engine when driving faster or always driving at the same speed. During heavy physical exercise we automatically breathe up to 80 times per minute. However, such is the flexibility of our conscious breathing, that someone experienced in breathwork can inhale the same volume of oxygen while breathing only 4–8 times per minute.

Our ability to control the breathing pattern is also one of the factors that makes it possible for us to experience and express emotions. Without a flexible breathing pattern we would find it difficult to distinguish between sadness and joy, hatred and love; according to the quality of our breathing we experience some emotions as heavy and limiting and others as light and liberating. The breath is also our main contact with the outer world. When we inhale we take in new energy from the outside world — we get 'inspired.' When we exhale we empty out our inner environment and open up to the world outside and its unknown qualities. So to breathe fully is to live fully. When we breathe openly and freely we are open to the world around us. We are one with our environment.

This unity with the environment is more than just an expression. It happens quite literally. Every breath we take contains around one million particles that have existed in our environment since the beginning of time and which certainly at some point in time have passed through every living being on our planet — including Buddha, Jesus, Hitler and Einstein. Every time we breathe out we add something unique to the surrounding atmosphere. Every time we exhale we also add to our planet's natural life cycle. The oxygen we breathe in is actually a waste product of plants and what we breathe out as carbon dioxide is nutrition for plants. And — as we shall see later on — we also breathe a more subtle form of life energy which links with an even higher cosmic life cycle.

The downside of the great flexibility and conscious intervention which we can exercise over our breathing is that we generally lose our natural breathing pattern as we become adults. The main reason for this is the close link between the way we breathe and what is going on in our minds. Since the breath is our main way of regulating impressions from the outside world, we would need an ideal environment to effortlessly maintain the ideal breathing pattern. For those of us who live in the modern western world, the environment is far from ideal. Consequently, a majority of adults suffer from more or less permanent breathing disorders. It is interesting to note, as well, that at about the same time as the current scientific worldview was first introduced to the western world, new types of food were being brought into Europe from other continents. In particular various new forms of stimulants such as coffee, tea, chocolate and tobacco were introduced to the western world. One factor that these stimulants have in common is that they influence our breathing pattern in a negative way.

In order to endure the stress to which our modern lifestyles expose our bodies, we breathe less than optimally for large parts of our waking lives, and this process of restricting the breath can begin from the very first breath we take. As we grow up the inadequacy of our breathing becomes more and more permanent and we cease to remember what it was like to breathe fully. The only symptoms we may notice are a gradual diminution of the overall functions of the body, leaving us with a general sense of imbalance and lifelessness. Insufficient breathing is like running a car on poorly refined petrol — even if it keeps running the performance is diminished.

Insufficient breathing

This lack of awareness among most adults as to how poor and insufficient their breathing pattern is — and the effect this is having on their wellbeing — is another consequence of our neglect of the breath in the West. Research shows that most adults utilize only 10–20 per cent of their total breathing capacity. Even healthy people often only breathe in about a third of the oxygen that their bodies need to function optimally. Generally, the consequences of insufficient breathing go unnoticed, leading to minor problems that are rarely consciously linked to poor breathing. Not until the effects have accumulated over many years will they start to be noticeable. The first signs are normally a general decrease in the bodily functions. Temporarily this may have no serious effects on the body. Unfortunately, too little is known about the long-term effects of insufficient breathing to be certain about the real consequences, but research indicates that a number of the age-related illnesses are (partly at least) the effects of insufficient breathing. These conditions include; allergies, asthma, cancer, circulatory problems, diabetes, epilepsy, headaches and migraine, hypertension (often causing high blood pressure), peptic ulcers and sexual organ dysfunction.

Breath rehabilitation

An obvious first step to rehabilitating our breathing is to become aware of how we are breathing — and how often we breathe in a limited and restricted way. But, unfortunately, simple awareness may not always be enough: If our insufficient breathing pattern has become permanent and well-established, our ability to breathe naturally has diminished. We simply can't remember how to breathe correctly anymore, and, in addition, the muscles that control the breathing apparatus may have lost their natural vigour and strength. Just as with the rest of the body's muscles, we may need to consciously re-train these muscles in order to regain our natural breathing capacity. Conventional wisdom tells us that if we break an arm or a leg the affected muscles need to be retrained in order to regain their strength and functionality, and, in fact, the same applies to the musculature which controls breathing.

Only when we consciously start to improve our breathing pattern do we truly realize how great the difference can be between good and poor breathing. One of the main benefits of proper breathing is improved circulation. Blood flow to all the internal organs increases and, consequently, they function better. Muscle tone also improves and our thoughts get clearer and more positive, partly because of the increased flow of oxygenated blood to the brain. According to the American breathing instructor, Carola Speads, it is the breath that ultimately determines how well a person functions in life. She claims that:

> Good breathing habits should be established early in
> life. Mothers and all those who care for infants

should be alert to the process of breathing recovery. Most people who pick up a baby in distress think they can lay the infant down as soon as he has stopped crying. But they should hold the baby closely, continuing to pat his back and comfort him, until he draws a deep breath. Only then has the infant's breathing normalised itself, and only then should you lay him down. This is a process so easy to observe that anyone alerted to it cannot possibly miss it. Good breathing habits, instead of poor ones, would thus be promoted.[2]

Everything is forgone by the mind,
Led by the mind,
Created by the mind.

Dhammapada

The influence of the mind

Since our breathing is controlled by the mind, it may be necessary to establish which thoughts and emotions are restricting our breathing. We need to recognize that restricted breathing is not simply the result of chance or bad habits — restricting the breath is one of our defence mechanisms against negative influences in our lives; it is a bodily defence against inner imbalance. This is something we need to respect if we are to restore our natural breathing. So, rehabilitating the breath involves both the process of regaining the physical ability to breathe naturally and the search for the psychological reasons why we restricted the breathing in the first place. This will almost certainly require identifying and analysing our deepest thoughts, emotions and attitudes to life. It is only when we get in touch with these that we are really able to change our breathing patterns in a positive and permanent way.

The importance of the exhalation

When we describe optimal breathing, we are usually mainly concerned about how much air we breathe in. We generally care less about how much air we breathe out. Still, exhalation is crucial for optimal breathing and is, in fact, the part of the breathing cycle that can cause the most problems. One explanation is that stress leads to tension in the muscles, which actually makes it easier to inhale than to exhale: when we breathe in we tense the muscles in the diaphragm and around the ribcage. When we breathe out we relax the muscles we used to inhale. So, under constant stress, we are actually unable to relax enough to exhale properly. The psychiatrist, Magda Proskauer, was one of the first to realize the importance of proper exhalation. She writes:

> Our incapacity to exhale naturally seems to parallel the psychological condition in which we are often filled with old concepts and long-since-consumed ideas, which just like the air in our lungs, are stale and no longer of any use.[3]

Proskauer concludes that, in order to improve our breathing, we need to release ourselves from the mental burdens we carry. When we get rid of this weight on our shoulders we automatically relax and drop the shoulders to their natural position rather than keeping them tensed and raised (which is one of the most obvious outward signs of stress). When the shoulders are relaxed natural breathing becomes much easier.

When we exhale, it is not just carbon dioxide that we are breathing out: the stagnant body energy that we exhale contains old tensions, thoughts and emotions. And when we breathe in we are not just taking in oxygen. We are also absorbing new impressions from the external world, which then generate new thoughts and emotions. Our breathing, therefore, has rightly been compared with a constant alternation between dying and being reborn: when we breathe out we allow the old to die and when we breathe in we are reborn with new impressions.

Without mastering breathing nothing can be mastered.

G.I. Gurdjieff

A quick breath test

How's your breathing? Is it restricted? Are you breathing optimally? For a quick (and crude) answer to these questions, let me suggest the following exercise to assess how you are breathing: sit comfortably on a chair with both feet on the ground and the back as straight as possible. Loosen any clothes that may restrict your breathing, and also ensure that your sitting posture is not having any restrictive effect on your breathing. Place one hand on your chest and the other on your stomach, covering the navel. Without changing anything, pay attention to how you are breathing. How are your hands moving as you breathe in and out? Do both hands move at the same time and with small movements? If so you are breathing mainly in the chest — which is only half of the full breathing movement. Does the lower hand move inwards and the upper hand upwards when you breathe in, and the opposite when you breathe out? If so your breathing pattern is reversed which also indicates a certain constriction. Does the upper hand remain almost still while the lower hand moves in and out? If so you are using all of the breathing apparatus — which is your natural breathing pattern. How many breaths are you taking per minute? If more than 14, you are breathing too rapidly for such a calm activity. But please be aware that it is difficult to breathe naturally when consciously focusing on and counting your breaths, so don't panic if the results seem negative.[4]

The quality of our breathing

The way we breathe reveals a lot about our general outlook on life. How much and how freely we breathe reflects how willing we are to meet life around us. How we exhale shows how willing we are to trust what happens to us and to go with the flow of life. If we feel unhappy about ourselves and our situation, our first reaction is often to restrict our breathing. In this way we limit our interaction with the outer world and make it easier for us to maintain the inner world we have created for ourselves. It is in our nature to express happiness and harmony with openness and trust. When we are happy and content we have little reason to shut out and restrict. Happiness is living in the now, and, when happy, the future probably seems equally bright. So it is not happiness and harmony we are trying to keep away. It is rather feelings of fear, mistrust, anger and other negative emotions. It is not that we really want to keep the negative feelings but rather that we worry about what will come next. We know what we have but we don't know what the future holds for us.

Chest tapping

A simple way to facilitate your breathing is to tap gently on the chest. Bring together the fingers as if you are holding a pea. Tap gently on the chest bones, either from the top down or in the opposite direction. Follow the rounded contour of the ribcage — one side at a time — right hand on left side and reverse. Do not tap too hard. This makes the muscles stiff whereas a gentle tap will make them relaxed. Try tapping your legs a couple of times before you start if you are uncertain of how hard to tap. Try to tap rhythmically. This creates a positive vibration. Avoid areas that are tender and stop tapping if it makes you cough. (But try again later). To massage the chest by tapping the ribcage is a simple and effective way to increase the energy in the body through the breath.[5]

We can also read our emotions simply by looking at our breathing pattern. In his book *The Tao of Natural Breathing*, Dennis Lewis describes how different emotions have different breathing patterns. Anger has a short inhale and strong exhale (just like an angry bull). Anger also leads to tensed muscles, in particular in the neck, jaws, chest and hands. Fear has a short breathing pattern with fast and irregular breaths, leading to 'knots' in the stomach. Sadness has jerky, sobbing and superficial breathing patterns, which create a feeling of emptiness in the stomach. Impatience has a short, jerky and incoherent breathing pattern, which generates tensions in the chest. Guilt has a restricted, suffocating breathing pattern, leading to a feeling of heaviness in the whole body. Boredom has a short and lifeless breathing pattern, which creates the feeling that the whole body is lifeless. Positive emotions on the other hand — such as love, friendship and compassion are associated with a deep and comfortable breathing pattern and a feeling of openness and life-giving energy throughout the body.

In other words, our breathing expresses what is happening in our body. And this works both ways: by changing our breathing pattern we can influence what we think and feel. To put it another way; breath is engaged in a constant exchange process with the body and the mind. This two-way causality is the foundation for both old and new breathwork techniques — it is what makes it possible for breathwork to promote a healthy body and mind.

According to Indian tradition it is the actual breathing pattern — the rhythm, speed and volume of each breath — that has a direct influence on the body and mind. By changing the breathing pattern you can influence and change the body's inner energy flow. It is this flow that ultimately determines how well we are and how well the body functions. In other words the breath has an essential influence on the body's whole metabolism. It also controls the mind through influencing the pattern in the energy flow that passes through the mind. The breath and the mind are interdependent. If one retains the breath, his mind starts becoming one-pointed; if the breath is irregular and jerky, the mind is dissipated.[6]

Walking breathing exercise

This exercise is best done outdoors in beautiful weather. Walk with your back straight and shoulders and jaws relaxed. Breathe normally. Start counting two to three steps when you breathe in next time. Breathe through the nose so softly, slowly and gently as you can. Breathe out while counting two to three steps. Repeat this as long as you feel comfortable. Complete the exercise and return to normal breathing. Notice the difference in your body.

Sighing and yawning

There are other ways in which our breathing expresses how we feel. The most common expressions are yawning and sighing. These behaviours — and the meanings implicit in them — are so universal that they are included in social etiquette: yawning indicates lack of interest and sighing can express irritation, disapproval or hopelessness, so (like swearing) they are, in most cultures, to be avoided in polite society.

But yawning and sighing are not just forms of social signalling. They're also one of the body's mechanisms for immediately increasing its oxygen supply. When we are bored or tired we breathe less than usual. And vice versa — when we under-breathe we get tired and lose interest in what we are doing. In order to regain a higher performance level, as quickly as possible, the body triggers a spontaneous and strong contraction in the diaphragm. This forces us to take a deeper breath than normal. Yawning is often also linked with an urge to stretch the body. The explanation, again, is that when we stretch the arms and upper part of the body, we automatically take deeper and easier breaths.

The reflex to yawn continues to be activated until the

body has regained balance between oxygen and carbon dioxide. So, instead of regarding yawning as a negative social signal, maybe we ought to start seeing it as very positive that the tired person in our company has triggered an acute action in order to regain their vitality and interest as quickly as possible.

Sighing is a closely related method of increasing the body's oxygen supply. Again, it indicates that the person's breathing is not as efficient as it could be. In a social context we regard sighing as a sign of irritation and/or general negativity and it is generally connected with poor psychological health. This is often a correct observation. But people who sigh are probably also suffering from poor breathing, and, unfortunately this two-way effect is not commonly recognized. A person who does not feel well psychologically is usually breathing too little and a person who is under-breathing is more likely to be affected by poor psychological health than people who breathe adequately.

Breathing exercise for waking up in the morning
While you are still in bed, lift both arms and point with both fingers towards a point above the head. Let your eyes follow the fingers and breathe deeply and calmly for a few breaths.

Breathing exercise for falling asleep in the evening
Sit by the bedside with both feet on the floor and straight back. Lean the head back as slowly as possible. The mouth will then open automatically. Breathe with your mouth open and keep breathing until the head has reached as far back as it will get. Change direction and keep breathing while moving the head back to the starting position (with straight back, not forward). Repeat this exercise three times.[7]

The scent of the breath

The breath can give rise to another negative social signal — in the form of bad breath. Having pleasant smelling breath is regarded as a positive social attribute. Bad breath, on the other hand, is something we all want to hide — much to the satisfaction of dentists and the cosmetics industry. Bad breath is caused by bacteria in the mouth. These are in fact an integral part of our digestive system. They are anaerobic bacteria whose task is to break down proteins in the food along with dead body tissue in the mouth. Under certain conditions, they can increase the speed of this breakdown process in a negative way leading to bad breath.

Bad breath test

A great difficulty with bad breath is that we may be blissfully unaware of it while to those around us it is only too apparent. There are, however, practical ways to assess the smell of the air we are breathing out. Here are some well-established tips:

1. Slide a cotton tip over the tongue's upper side and smell it.
2. Lick the back of the hand and let it dry before you smell the hand.
3. Floss between the teeth in the back of the mouth and smell the floss.
4. Stand in front of a mirror and stick out the tongue as far as you can. If the back of the tongue is white it may mean that you have bad breath.
5. Ask somebody you trust to give you an honest answer.[8]

Some consequences of incorrect breathing

Even though most adults in the stressful western world suffer from poor breathing, a majority of people are unaware of this. On the other hand, they are probably well aware of the indirect consequences; infections, poor digestion, constipation, ulcers and other digestive problems, depression, sexual disorders, sleep disorders, poor circulation, tiredness and overall low performance. In other words a number of common complaints, which most adults suffer from at some point in their lives — but, again, most people are completely unaware that these disorders are linked to their breathing pattern.

A clear example of the influence of breathing is its effects on digestion: for the body to digest the food properly it requires an even and relaxed abdominal breathing pattern. This facilitates digestion by promoting movements in the stomach and intestine and increasing blood supply, all of which assists our ability to extract nutrition from the food we eat. To achieve this we need to sit down and eat in peace and quiet. Ideally, a period of rest should follow after the meal. To eat while standing or walking, or to be exposed to stress in other ways during a meal, is a quick and effective way of getting stomach cramps or worse. Chronically disturbed digestion is a common phenomenon in today's fast food culture, as a result of too many stressful meals.

A number of medical disorders have very direct effects on breathing, for example asthma and hyperventilation. Hyperventilation is the medical term for the situation which may occur when we try to control our breath by forcing the exhale. The unintended effect of this is to acutely stimulate the urge to breathe in order to compensate for having breathed out too much air. As we will see later in the book, hyperventilation, paradoxically, leads to acute breathlessness, often resulting in panic. In reality, however, this experienced inability to breathe is a natural reaction of the body in order to restore balance. Often the symptoms are so severe and inexplicable that people suffering from hyperventilation end up in the emergency reception of their local

Another brief 'breath test'

The first test was designed to establish your breathing pattern. Now we can consider some more subtle aspects of the way you breathe. (You may want to note the results on a bookmark, for reference further into the book.)

As before, sit comfortably on a chair with both feet on the ground and the back as straight as possible. Loosen any clothes that may restrict your breathing, and also ensure that your sitting posture is not having any restrictive effect on your breathing. Close your eyes and turn your attention inwards without changing your breathing pattern.

Continue to breathe as normal and pay attention to how you are breathing. Become aware of how the air is moving in your body. Is it moving more easily in some parts than others? Which parts of the body are involved in your breathing? Which parts of the body are being reached by your breath? How does your breathing feel? Is it easy or difficult? Does it feel good or bad? How do you inhale? Is your inhaling strained or easy and open? Are you breathing sufficiently? Is your breathing as open as it should be? How is your exhaling? Is it effortless or do you have to strain to get the air out of your lungs? Is your abdomen relaxed when you exhale? Do you give yourself enough time to exhale before you inhale? How long is the pause between inhaling and exhaling? What are your thoughts and feelings about your breathing? Does it feel good or are you concerned about your observations?

Answer truthfully and avoid judgements. Remember that the objective is to assess the present quality of your breathing. If you want to improve on this, it is essential to have an accurate idea of your personal starting point.

hospital. In such situations hyperventilation may not always be accurately diagnosed, however, despite the unreliable statistics, there is evidence emergencies of this kind are increasing. According to Fried, 60 per cent of all emergency ambulance transports in America's larger cities involve hyperventilation or other breath-related disorders.[9] Another American study indicates that 10 to 25 per cent of the USA's population suffer from breath-related illness every year. Despite all the evidence, many medical staff still fail to consider breathing disorders when making diagnoses. The real figures on the connection between breathing and illness are, therefore, very hard to assess. At the same time, a growing number of scientists are demonstrating direct links between poor breathing and life-threatening illnesses such as cancer and heart problems.

Environmental influence

The environment also clearly has a significant impact on our breathing. Unlimited access to 'fresh,' clean air is the ideal. But unfortunately few people these days can say that the air they breathe is clean and pollution-free. For people who live in large cities, spending a day in the countryside can often graphically illustrate the poor quality of the air they normally breathe. The effect of the cleaner country air can be quite noticeable. In the fresher air people have more energy and experience a 'lighter mind.' They may also become unaccustomedly tired in the evening and sleep a lot better than they do in their city environment.

The indoor environment also has an effect on our breathing. Air-conditioning and overly effective insulation make the air dry, especially during cold winters. This can cause excessive drying of the mucous membranes, which, in turn, impairs the body's ability to dispose of internal debris, such as dirt particles and bacteria. This can lead to deposits of mucous that cause further restrictions in the body's internal cleaning processes. An effective solution to problems of this kind is the use of air moisturisers. On very cold days the indoor air can get exceptionally dry. Cold weather also makes it unpleasant to breathe. For sensitive people, cold air can give rise to asthmatic symptoms.

Household chemicals are another potential source of irritants for the airways, leading to breathing dysfunction. A particular culprit is the spray in all its forms. Consequently, all air freshener products are best avoided. The best methods for keeping the air fresh are simply to open windows and keep rooms clean. Other air-borne pollutants which can cause breathing difficulties, in particular for sensitive and/or allergic people, are; dust, pollen, fungus, pets, certain food particles and preservatives.

A 'mega' cause of breathing problems, which outweighs all others by far is, of course, smoking. It is well established that even very sporadic smoking leads to decreased lung capacity. Passive smoking is no exception. On the contrary, it is even more dangerous than active smoking because the smoke inhaled contains higher levels of harmful and carcinogenic substances.

A short breathing exercise to clear the mind

This exercise will make your exhale freer and less forced. You will need a straw to breathe through for this exercise. Sit with your feet on the ground and the back as straight as possible. Wait until your breathing has become calm and unrestricted. Breathe through the nose. Pay attention to when you inhale and exhale. When you start exhaling, put the straw in your mouth and continue the exhale through the straw instead of through the nose. Remove the straw just before you complete the exhale. Repeat the exercise a couple of times. Avoid forcing the exhale. Notice how well you succeed and remember to compare this each time you do this exercise.[10]

For it is only when we can be aware of
both our inner and outer worlds
at the same time,
that we can go beyond the beliefs
of our self-image and experience the real forces at work in us.

Dennis Lewis

Inner and outer breathing

So far we have been mainly concerned with those aspects of breathing that are well accepted in the western world, namely, breathing as a physiological process which supplies the body with oxygen. But we can also breathe in more conscious and systematic ways, with specific purposes in mind. It is these more controlled ways of breathing which are referred to under the generic term 'breathwork.' What the different forms of breathwork have in common is a conscious changing of the breathing pattern for a specific reason. One definition is that: *Breathwork is the intentional alteration of the breathing pattern for healing and mind-expanding purposes.*

According to the ancient eastern traditions, breathing as a physiological process is only 'outer breathing.' In addition there is also 'inner breathing.' This is a more subtle form of breathing that vitalizes all parts of the body and psyche. As we will see later on, the eastern cultures have a very different view of the way the body functions. In the East, in order to improve the quality of the breathing, it is just as important to become aware of the inner breathing as the outer. By increasing our awareness of how the inner breath moves around in our body, and affects its various parts, we can learn more about ourselves. In particular, about the parts of the body of which we are normally unaware.

According to the eastern traditions, the most important function of the breath is also to supply the body with vital 'energy.' However, they mean by this much more than simply delivering oxygen. We will look more closely at the concept of 'life energy' later on, but here we can note its importance for inner breathing. In the eastern traditions, energy moves up towards the head when we breathe in and down through the whole body when we breathe out. When we breathe in we also absorb energy from the earth through our feet and then on up through the body. When we breathe out we are disposing not only of toxins but also of 'used' or stagnant energy. Also, we can take in energy from the surrounding space when we inhale and bring it down from the head through the body when we exhale. This energy exchange between earth and heaven will supply us with vital 'life energy' which is believed to have a positive effect on all the body functions.

In the eastern worldview the polarity between heaven and earth is seen as vital for all living organisms; we depend not just on the chemical and electrical influences within and outside our bodies, but also on the electromagnetic polarity between earth and atmosphere. Our bodies act as conductors within this electromagnetic field, with the head as the positive pole and the feet as the negative. Since these effects are decreased by exposure to air pollution or confined spaces, this is one of the reasons why it is important to have access to fresh air and open spaces.

The process of breathing, if we can begin to understand it
in relation to the whole of life,
shows us the way to let go of the old and open to the new.
Dennis Lewis

Semantics

We'll look more closely at the history of attitudes to breathing in later chapters, but to convey a sense of how great the difference is between the modern West and earlier cultures in this respect, we'll conclude this overview by looking at accounts of breath and breathing in a few different cultures. In particular, examining the origin of the words used to describe breathing and its effects can indicate the importance which earlier cultures attached to the breath.

Most languages have expressions as to how our pattern of breathing is related to impressions from the outer world. For example, we become 'breathless' or have our breath 'taken away' not just when we are physically exhausted but also when we see something beautiful, or experience intense fear, surprise, love, pain etc. We can also note that before the modern western world split body and soul apart, breath also had a spiritual dimension. This is reflected in the fact that the words for 'breathe' and 'spirit' have the same origin in many languages, as in the Latin verb *spirare* where we find the root for the words: spirit, respiration, inspiration, and so on. In an image which reflects how the divine breathes life into the created world, Christianity equals the *Holy Spirit* with the *Father* and the *Son* in a divine trinity.

The Semitic and Indo-European languages are considered to be among the world's oldest, and they've had a major influence on many of the world's great religious and philosophical systems. The Hebrew word *nephesh* (breathing) has links with all the meanings of life, soul and spirit. Equally, the words *ruach*, *neshamah* and *baraka* are linked with breathing and spirit. In Arabic the words *nefs* and *ruh* have a similar meaning. In Sanskrit (the religious language of India) the word *atman* (soul) is linked with breathing. The Greek words *psyche* and *pneuma* have the same relationship. The Greeks also used the word *diaphragm* (the muscle that pumps in air to the body) both for the mind and for breathing. In Slavic languages the word *duch*, which derives from the word for 'breathing,' means soul or spirit. In gypsy dialect the work *duk* means breathing, soul or spirit.

In Germanic languages such as Swedish, the words *andas* (to breathe) and *ande* (spirit) have the same close relationship. The English word *breathe* on the other hand has a different root. It stems from the Germanic word *braeth* that means odour or exhalation. This in turn is linked with the words *brawn* (strong muscle) and *brood* (something produced by means of warmth) — one aspect hinting at the breathing apparatus, the other at some effect of breathing.

Among Australian aborigines the word *waug* means: breathing, spirit and soul. Among the Netela-speaking Indians of California the word *piuts* means: life, breathing and soul. In Java the word *nawa* stands for: breathing, life and soul.

Many cultures also have words expressing the concept of life energy. In India this energy is called *prana*. In Tibet it is called *lung* and in China *Qi* (sometimes spelled *chi*). The nomad people of the Kalahari Desert also recognize this concept and have the word *n/um* while the Sioux Indians call it *ney-atoneyah*.

2. The Power of the Breath

There must be some primal force,
But it is impossible to locate.
I believe it exists, but cannot see it.
I see its results,
I can even feel it,
But it has no form.
  Zhuang Zi, Inner Chapters, *fourth century* BC

The best-kept traditions of how to use the full power of the breath are mainly from the Asian countries of China, India, Japan and Tibet. As a result, the breath has a very different role in these countries. Breathing is used for healing and maintaining good health, as well as for spiritual advancement.

China alone has several thousand breathing techniques aimed at achieving very precisely defined results, both for physical and spiritual purposes. Because much of the teaching of these techniques is done personally from master to single pupil, it is impossible to establish the exact number. This one-to-one teaching is undertaken because the more advanced techniques can produce powerful effects, and to keep the teaching as safe as possible, the master alone can decide when an individual student is ready for it.

It is hard to establish exactly how long people have known about the potential in our breath. The first written accounts describe well-established breathing techniques that may have taken thousands of years to develop. Most likely is that they date back to prehistoric times. There has also been a continuing exchange of knowledge between the old cultures in eastern and western Asia and the Mediterranean countries — but which of the breathwork 'schools' is the oldest is now impossible to establish.

The role of breathwork in China

China has two major religions or philosophies — Taoism and Buddhism. Both have a religious aspect and a more general one that has an impact on everyday life in China. Despite their different origin, both philosophies have substantial knowledge of the power and potential of the breath. It is mainly the Taoist breathing techniques that are identified with China, but the Buddhist tantric breathing techniques are also widespread.

Taoism (sometimes spelled Daoism) offers detailed explanations for the use of breathwork as a spiritual tool, as well as practical methods for maintaining physical and mental wellbeing. A reason for this is that when Taoism was first developed during Emperor Huang Ti's rule around 2700 BC, the maintenance of good mental and physical health was regarded as part of spiritual development, and in order to achieve this, a range of breathing exercises was developed. Chinese monks, too, have always used the breath to reach a higher level of consciousness.

According to Taoism, increased awareness of the inner world is achieved simply by observing how the air we breathe mixes with the world outside. Through passively observing how the air and the body move in harmony with the breathing rhythm, we can learn how thoughts and emotions influence us and how we interact with the world around us both on the material and the esoteric level.

This led to the development of a range of very precise breathing exercises. Some estimate the number of different methods to be around 3000, while others say it is closer to 10,000. Collectively they are known as *Qigong* (or Chi Kung). *Qi* is the Chinese name for life energy — a concept that lacks a counterpart in the West. (Some readers may be more familiar with the Indian equivalent *prana*). *Gong* refers to the power to achieve an effect through repeated exercises. Literally, qigong can be translated as energy cultivation. The breathing exercises in qigong are also known as 'methods of eliminating illness and prolonging life.' Another common translation is 'achieving life-force.'

Qigong is continually developing. Many of the exercises that now have spread to the West are relatively new — from the beginning of the twentieth century and more recently. A group of exercises that have spread widely in the West are known as Tai Chi — sometimes called shadow boxing since the movements resemble a slow form of boxing.

... when we are able to breathe through our whole body,
sensing our verticality from head to foot,
we are aligning ourselves with the natural flow of energy
connecting heaven and earth.

Dennis Lewis

Aspects of qigong

Most qigong exercises are done slowly so the mind has time to register the movement throughout the body, resulting in a relaxing effect. Many exercises are designed to facilitate breathing, and the circulation of oxygen-rich blood throughout the body. At the same time, however, improved and increased breathing also leads to improved mental concentration. Thoughts become clearer and the mind calmer, and the thought process slows down. With the mind less preoccupied with thoughts it gets more time to focus on keeping the mind and body healthy.

A person's physical and spiritual development is divided in four basic principles involving breathing, body, sound and mind.

Breathing

Breathing is divided into three different forms. The most common is the balanced breathing pattern where the inhale has the same length as the exhale. This is our common breathing pattern, regardless of how much or how little we breathe. It is automatic and unconscious and suitable for everyday situations.

The second breathing pattern is the cleansing breath with an emphasis on the exhale. A spontaneous expression is sighing which is initiated by stagnation or tension in the body. By extending the exhale we can relax and rid the body of stagnant energy.

The third breathing pattern is the energizing breath where the inhale is greater than the exhale. A spontaneous expression is yawning which brings more energy into the tired or inactive body.

T'ai I chin Hua Tsung (The Secret of the Golden Flower), one of the ancient Chinese scriptures, was written on wooden plates in the seventeenth century, after being orally transmitted for a long time. On one of them it is inscribed:

> Master Lu-Stu said, That which exists through itself is called the Way (Tao). Tao has neither name nor shape. It is the one essence, the one primal spirit. Essence and life cannot be seen. They are contained in the light of heaven. The light of heaven cannot be seen ... The great One is the term given to that which has nothing above it ... If man attains this One he becomes alive; if he loses it he dies. But even if man lives in the energy (vital breath) he does not see the energy, just as fishes live in the water but do not see the water. Man dies when he has no vital breath, just as fishes perish when deprived of water.[11]

The body

The second aspect of human development deals with the importance of the body for our general wellbeing. By training the body to sit, stand and move internal circulation is improved. This is an important factor in the absorption of the oxygen that the breath introduces. It is important not to cut off the circulation when standing or walking, and a part of

Qigong is aimed at learning how to stand and sit. The various movements are mainly aimed at directly or indirectly stimulating certain areas of the body to improve the circulation.

For instance, the basic principles for standing begin with the position of the pelvis. In order to keep the pelvis in the right place, the knees need to be relaxed. To unlock the knees, the feet must be in the right place. The same applies for the back and head that need to be aligned in order to maintain the correct position and openness throughout the body. If the head is held correctly the shoulders will relax, etc. The principle is to utilize the skeleton to maintain the body upright so that the muscles can relax and allow full circulation throughout the body. In order to maintain the skeleton upright without the help of muscles, the body needs to be properly aligned.

Sound

Like all substances in the universe, the body is constantly vibrating, through the constant movement of the molecules in the body. Since sound is vibration on a certain frequency, sounds are often used to facilitate relaxation in the body.

The mind

The mind is the most important part of qigong. Since the mind is unlimited, the body, breath and voice are trained so that they can influence the mind. When mind control is practised so often that it becomes automatic, we increase our life energy and inner harmony. The goal for qigong is to reach Great Wisdom and to realize the Real Truth in cosmos.

Empty yourself of everything.
Let the mind become still.
The ten thousand things rise and fall while the Self watches
*   their return.*
They grow and flourish and then return to the source.
Returning to the source is stillness, which is the way of nature ….
Tao Te Ching, Lao Tse, sixth century BC

Relaxation

One of the basic principles of qigong is to increase relaxation. When we relax, the body gets softer and less tensed; the mind gets calmer and clearer; and the body works better and in greater harmony with nature. Relaxation techniques are very important, and are aimed mainly at co-ordinating body posture and breathing with the mind, so that the whole functions in balance and harmony.

Fangsong Gong

A basic relaxation exercise in qigong is called Fangsong Gong — a breathing exercise aimed at reducing nervous tension and vitalizing the mind. It is particularly valuable for people with high blood pressure. The relaxation increases mostly at the exhale, since some muscles have to contract in order to bring air in to the body.

Sit on a chair with both feet on the ground and hands lightly resting on the knees. Close the eyes and breathe calmly in a normal way for a few moments. Imagine that the body starts to relax — part by part. Start at the top and visualize each part of the body (head, eyes, ears, nose, mouth, neck etc.). Move first down the front of the body and then do the same with the back. Repeat the process a couple of times until the body feels light, relaxed and comfortable.

Then start to visualize the Chinese word *song,* either by saying it silently inside yourself or aloud each time you exhale. Feel how the vibration spreads through the body, bringing an increased sense of relaxation and wellbeing.

The word *song* literally means 'loose.' But the important part is the pronunciation. It starts with the s-sound where the teeth touch each other and the tongue is pressed gently against the teeth while the air passes to make the *ssss*-sound. Then the teeth are opened to let the air pass to form the *ong*-sound that sounds like a bell. Repeat this sound a couple of times. Terminate the exercise.

The three treasures

The basis of Taoism is the ancient principle that when sky and earth meet, life occurs. According to Chinese mythology, the human body is 'made of breaths.' At the beginning of time there were nine different forms of breath that together formed chaos. When chaos was dissolved the breaths were separated. The pure and subtle breaths formed the sky, and the impure and stronger breaths formed the earth. The first major gods were formed from 'knots' in the breaths. Since humankind is created from impure breaths we must replace our breath with the pure form.

Equally our physical wellbeing is directly linked to having a free and open flow of three different forces — the earth force, the cosmic force and the universal force. The earth force and cosmic force correspond to the forces of nature and our higher self, while the universal force is energy created in space. These forces manifest in the body in the form of three different substances or 'treasures' that correspond to three aspects of human behaviour. They are *Jing* (or *Ching*) representing earth, body, and yin; *Qi*, representing life, mind and harmony; and *Shen* representing heaven, spirit and yang. This is how the thirteenth century Master Li describes it in *The Book of Balance and Harmony*:

> Jing naturally transforms into Qi,
> Qi naturally transforms into Spirit,
> and Spirit naturally transforms into pure openness,
> uniting with cosmic space.
> This is called returning to the root,
> returning to origin.
> The path of everlasting life and eternal vision is complete.

Jing

Jing (or essence-of-life) stands for the body's real essence or fundamental material. We get this force from two sources. One, that we are born with is known as *innate jing,* and is the inheritance from our ancestors; the other comes from nutrition and is called *acquired jing.* In order to optimize the intake of Qi, the quality of the food and air we consume is important. Abundance of jing means strong vitality whereas depletion of jing leads to weakened immune system and lower physical vitality. The two are mixed in the body and stored mainly in the stomach and kidney area. The mixture of innate and acquired jing in the kidneys has strong links with sexual energy and reproduction. Certain breathing exercises are directly aimed at converting sexual energy to spiritual energy in a form of inner alchemy.

Qi

Qi (chi) is the vital, intrinsic substance in everything created in the whole of cosmos. It too is divided into innate and aquired Qi along the same lines as *jing*. The combination is known as *genuine Qi* and is the dynamic force of all vital human functions. Although we also get Qi from food, water and air, the various substances in themselves are not Qi. Qi is rather a kind of energy aspect of all substances.

We get Qi from the earth and nature around us, and from space above us. It is absorbed through the feet, skin, palms, top of the head and other energy points. This energy is transported around the body through a special circulation system employing meridians. This system is separate from — but similar to — the blood circulation. While this description of the body's energy circulation is common to all the eastern schools, it is not recognized by western medicine.

The way we breathe also determines how efficiently we absorb Qi, both directly, and indirectly by influencing the digestion of the food we eat. The two main ways of introducing energy through breathing, are through normal abdominal breathing, and through special breathing exercises. The normal, automatic, breathing pattern resembles the breathing in small children. The Taoist breathing pattern is sometime called reversed breathing since the belly moves inwards during inhalation and outwards during exhalation.

The main storage place for life energy in the body is in the area around the solar plexus, and this is also regarded as our emotional centre. The energy is mainly stored in the lower *Tan Tien* between the navel, kidneys and the upper part of the pubic bone. With a good supply of energy in this area it is easier to absorb energy in other forms. It acts as a kind of magnet that attracts energy from outside, by coordinating its vibrations with the surrounding world.

When the Tan Tien area is blocked, it gives a feeling of general weakness and imbalance. On the mental level, it can make us critical towards ourselves, and the world we live in. Also, despite constantly refilling this energy supply, its energy gets weaker as we get older.

It is important to maintain the body's Qi with the help of regular breathing exercises. If the body is not constantly supplied with new energy, the body's natural levels will get depleted, leading to stagnation and weakening of our body functions. But by our continually supplying the body with new Qi, the body's ability to function can be improved and this helps to counteract the weakening that comes with ageing.

Shen

The third treasure is *Shen* — the closest translation is 'spirit' or 'higher awareness.' This too is a substance or energy in the body that is either brought into the body, or is a natural part of the body. Shen is closely linked with the heart and is our individual expression for awareness and soul activity. It is also referred to as heavenly Qi since Shen has its origin among the stars.

The main storage space for Shen is in the upper Tan Tien — the area between the eyebrows (where we also find the pineal gland). From this area the mental activity that influences the clarity of our thoughts and awareness is controlled. When we are open in this area, we have a strong and clear intuition, as well as clear goals in life. This shines through as clarity of our eyes. When this area is blocked, we have problems concentrating and making decisions. According to Chinese medicine, the patient needs to have stored sufficient Shen in order for the body to heal.

Although Shen appears naturally in the body, the high stress levels of modern societies deplete us of this resource, and this makes it difficult for us to obtain physical and spiritual regeneration. Shen can however be influenced through various exercises. One of the most efficient ways is to be in touch with the body's energy in the lower Tan Tien area (below the navel) and to keep this open and active through correct breathing — that is, deep abdominal breathing.

Makyo

In the *Zazen* or Zen meditation school the concept of *makyo* (*ma* meaning the devil, *kyo* the objective world) is described as diabolic phenomena occurring at some point, when meditation is used for spiritual development. *Makyo* is a mixture of real and unreal phenomena, similar to dreams. It includes visions, hallucinations, fantasies, dreams, pictures, sound, smell, or homeostatic changes (body temperature and sweating, etc), all of which are said to be caused by the breathing not being in harmony with the mind. When the mind has been stilled only partly, deeper-lying thoughts from the unconscious reach the surface and are expressed in pictures and visions.

Qi and negative ions

China has not experienced the same division between modern science and traditional knowledge that we have in the West, and for this reason it is much more common there for modern research methods to be used in the study of ancient breathing techniques. Among others, studies have been undertaken to establish the effects of negative and positive ions on the body. One result has been to develop specific breathing exercises where the breath is swallowed in order to release negative ions.

Ions are electrically charged particles in the air we breathe. The atmosphere surrounding us has an electrical charge that leads to the formation of positive and negative ions. The negative ions contain almost pure electric energy formed by the atmosphere's contact with energy from the sun, cosmic particles, thunderstorms, winds, the movement of water and the earth's natural radioactive radiation. They play an important role in our wellbeing.

Chinese studies have shown that special breathing exercises

lead to an unusual release of infrared radiation, static electricity and various particle streams from the air. They found that negative ions facilitate the transmission of oxygen and the removal of carbon dioxide. They also increase serotonin in the brain which gives a feeling of increased wellbeing.[12]

Techniques to increase the intake of negative ions are not unique to qigong. Similar research — apart from the breath-work aspect — is also conducted in the West. Studies have shown that negative ions are damaged by pollution and increased deforestation. They are also affected by electrical cables, concrete walls and other artificial structures that are common in our cities. Air in the countryside has a much higher content of negative ions, in particular near water, and high hills (common places for spas and health centres). The negative ions can also be increased mechanically, and this is commonly done, for example, in space capsules where special ionisers improve the air for the astronauts.

How to open the solar plexus

Sit or stand still for a few moments and become aware of your breathing. Then place your hands on the stomach area and visualize the energy stored inside the navel. Feel how it expands when you inhale and decreases when you exhale. Notice how your awareness can get deeply into the tissues around the navel. When you have been breathing with total concentration for a few breaths, start letting the energy grow when you inhale so that it reaches solar plexus (between the naval and chest). Feel how the solar plexus and the area around the navel contract when you exhale. Relax and feel the body's inner reaction. When you do this, the breathing will automatically slow down. Move the hands to the solar plexus and bend forward slightly. Notice how the breathing changes. Repeat this several times. Return to an upright position and focus your concentration on the solar plexus. Notice how the area expands and contracts with the breathing. Continue for a few more minutes. Terminate the exercise.

Breathwork and healing

In China, breathing exercises are a well-integrated part of traditional medicine. The oldest records of breathing exercises for medicinal purposes are from the Shang dynasty (1766–1123 BC).

The effects of breathing can be divided into three categories: effects on the body, effects on the psyche, and effects on the spirit. The variables which produce these effects are variations in the speed of breathing, the depth of each breath, and the length of each breath.

Quick Breathing

The physical effect of quick breathing is to speed up the metabolism, heartbeat and blood circulation. Psychologically, it provides an unstable and more easily affected state of mind, leading to faster emotional changes. Spiritually, it generates subjective and egocentric values and perceptions of the world, with greater emphasis on details.

Shallow Breathing

Here the metabolism becomes less active and there is less integration between its various functions. On the psychological level, shallow breathing produces a tendency to worry, mental instability and dissatisfaction, often leading to fear. Spiritually perception becomes superficial, with many distractions.

Slow breathing

The physical effect of slow breathing is to slow down the metabolism, heartbeat and blood circulation. Psychologically, it leads to a calmer, more peaceful state of mind, with clearer thoughts and more objective understanding. It also increases our sensitivity towards others. On the spiritual level, it leads to broader perception, deeper insights and a wider contact with universal consciousness.

Chinese breathing techniques

Over the centuries the Chinese have learnt to distinguish the most subtle nuances between the various types of breathing. As a result, they have developed a range of highly sophisticated breathing techniques, each evolved for use in a particular area of life. With the typical Chinese flair for lyrical expression, each technique is named after its intended effect. Here are some examples of slow breathing techniques.

The Breathing of Unselfishness

This is so still and slow that a piece of rice paper in front of the face will not move. It is meant to calm all bodily activities and to prepare for meditation. It is also used as a tool to recognize egocentric distortions in one's perception of the surrounding world.

The Breathing of Harmony

This pattern is slightly more powerful than the latter. It gives a peaceful and harmonic contact with the surrounding world and a greater awareness of it.

The Breathing of Self-Esteem

This is slightly faster than the previous ones. Its purpose is to enhance the harmony between the various bodily functions and give increased self-esteem.

The Breathing of Activity

Here each breath is long, deep and powerful, and taken through a slightly open mouth. Its purpose is to activate all physical, psychological and spiritual forces so that one can react to the surrounding world without losing objective perception. It is also used to release physical and psychological blockages and leads to general relaxation.

Deep Breathing

This causes the metabolism to become more active and more efficient and harmonic. Psychologically, it creates deep feelings of satisfaction, emotional stability and strong self-esteem. Spiritually, it leads to greater thoughtfulness, greater trust and openness and a more loving attitude. An example of deep breathing is called the Breathing of Spirituality. This pattern is long, deep and powerful. Breath is taken though the mouth, while forming the words *hi* (spirit, fire, sun) and *fu* (wind, expansion). It activates the physical and psychological metabolism and brings the person into contact with his or her spirituality.

Short Breaths

At the physical level, the metabolism becomes faster and more irregular. Psychologically, it leads to quicker changes of thought and emotion, with a tendency to greater impatience and shorter temper. Spiritually, it leads to greater disharmony with the surrounding world, and to contradictory and subjective opinions.

Long Breaths

At the physical level, this produces greater coordination between the various functions and metabolism. Activity in the organs and glands tends to become slower. Psychologically, long breaths create greater peacefulness and feelings of satisfaction, greater perseverance and a calmer temperament. Spiritually, they lead to deeper and more objective insights and understanding. Here are some examples of long breath forms.

—The Breathing of Intelligence: This is done in the throat and the area around the root of the tongue. Its purpose is to develop physical and psychological concentration. It gives a clear perception and deep insight into present problems.

—The Breathing of Tan-Tien: this is deep and slow, with natural movements of the diaphragm, which is regarded in Chinese anatomy as the centre of the body. The purpose of this pattern is to provide physical energy and psychological stability. It gives a feeling of steady anchoring on earth and makes it easier to stay uninfluenced by the surrounding world.

—The Breathing of Love: this is done in the upper part of the chest with a slow inhale and exhale. The inhale is about as long as the exhale and there should be no pause between them, so that the breathing proceeds in a natural gentle cycle. The purpose of this pattern is to make the heartbeat harmonious and the circulation of the blood and other bodily fluids more gentle. Psychologically, this form of breathing provides a feeling of harmony and love for all creation. It also makes for greater sensitivity, sympathy and understanding towards others. (This pattern has many similarities with the modern Rebirthing technique described below.)

How to release deep tensions

Become aware of your breathing. Feel how the air passes through the nose and the solar plexus area just above the navel. Visualize the air as a long silk thread that connects the whole front of your body from the nose down to the belly. Breathe through the mouth. The mouth should be almost closed and the exhale slow, calm and steady. Let out all the air in the lungs before you inhale again. Feel how the tension in the belly and solar plexus dissolves in the incoming air and disappears out with the outgoing air. Notice the solar plexus area and feel how it gets softer with every breath. Avoid looking for particular reactions with each individual breath — simply notice how the various parts of the body react. Observe calmly what happens in the body. Continue the exercise for another 15 to 20 minutes. Terminate the exercise.

Martial arts

In addition to the physical, medical and spiritual aspects of breathwork there is also a fourth aspect of breathwork in China. Very early on, conscious breathing exercises were used by soldiers to improve their strength and agility in combat. As they developed they were known under the collective name of *Wushu qigong*. At the outset they were exclusively used by Chinese soldiers, but in later years they have become increasingly popular with practitioners of martial arts both in Asia and in the West. Some of the most well-known are Kung Fu (Gongfu), Tai Chi Chuan, Hsing i Chuan and Ba Gua Chang.

All living creatures depend on the breath
For it is the sustaining force of life itself
Which determines how long all may live.
Those who revere breath as a gift from the Lord
Shall live to complete their full span of life.

Taittiriya Upanishad, seventh century BC

The role of breathwork in India

In India the tradition of consciously using the breath in various breathing techniques is as long established as it is in China. Here, too, it is used in healing and healthcare, as well as to provide a spiritual path. The method for maintaining and improving physical and spiritual wellbeing is known as *Yoga*, while the medical aspect is handled by *Ayur-Vedic* medicine. We will concentrate on the yoga aspect here, and come back to the medical aspect in a later chapter.

Exactly how old yoga is has not been established. It was probably created and developed, over many generations, by India's aboriginal population. The first evidence of yoga practices has been linked with the pre-Aryan Harappa culture which existed in the Indus Valley (now part of Pakistan) between 3000 and 1500 BC. This was an advanced civilization with a written language (which remains undeciphered) and comprehensive trade links with other groups of people.

Recent discoveries suggest however that yoga may be much older. Satellite pictures have revealed underwater cities off India's northwestern coast, estimated to be around 12,000 years old (based on knowledge of land changes in the area). Divers have found stone plates clearly illustrating various yoga stances.

When the Aryans invaded and conquered the Indus valley around 1500 BC, they absorbed much of the Harappa culture including the practice of yoga. Then during the fifth century BC a wave of movements concerned with spiritual development swept across the Indian subcontinent, and it was in the wake of this that the real development of yoga began. In the same period, Buddhism and Jainism evolved in India — and together with Hinduism and Islam they form India's principal religions.

The state of real absorption of consciousness,
which is beyond all knowledge, is yoga.

Akshyopanishad 2.3

Aspects of yoga

The word *Yoga* means 'union,' and has the same root as the English word 'yoke.' The union referred to is that between the cosmic forces and the channelling and controlling of an individual's own energies. In other words, the teaching is concerned with how one's own mental and physical powers can be linked with the universal forces that surround us. This view is shared with the Taoist philosophy, but has no comparison in the modern western worldview.

According to yoga teaching, everything in the universe is formed from the highest consciousness, that in turn guides everything in the universe. We come from here when we are born, and when we die we return. Everything in the universe is moving in and out of this consciousness in a constant wave movement. Creation is a process on many levels, starting from the highest where consciousness is formed. From consciousness the physical universe is formed; since consciousness wants to have a physical manifestation, the body is formed.

To begin with, yoga functioned as a practical complement to one of India's six classical philosophical systems, but gradually it developed into an independent philosophy in its own right. It is not known exactly when the first written description of classical yoga was produced, but it is known that the first named author, Patanjali, was not the founder of yoga, but simply described an existing body of theory.

Yoga can be described as a slow and thorough cleansing of body and soul. It employs several different methods to achieve this. The system of yoga described by Patanjali is nowadays called *Raja yoga* — the yoga of thought control. Its starting point, in the effort to reach a higher spiritual level, is the mind.

Raja yoga

Raja yoga, sometimes called the royal road of yoga, has eight different steps or paths to a higher spiritual consciousness. These involve social and personal rules of living, physical exercises, breathing exercises and spiritual exercises. All these steps aim exclusively at teaching the discipline of living required to achieve union with the absolute.

Hatha yoga

Hatha yoga is the yoga of body control. Hatha yoga's starting point is the body. The word *Hatha* is composed of *ha* (that stands for the sun, the positive energy or aspect, masculine form, and inhalation of breath), and *tha* (for the moon, the negative energy or aspect, feminine form and the exhalation of breath). *Ha* also represents the esoteric aspect and *tha* the body. The assumption behind Hatha yoga is that if the mind can influence the body, then the body can also influence the mind. (See Chapter 3 for a modern scientific view on this).

The basics of hatha yoga are a set of *asanas* (body positions or stances) aimed at increasing relaxation and inner peace, so that the body can benefit from the exercises. As in Tai Chi, the exercises are done slowly so that the body has time to register and absorb the full effect. Hatha yoga has spread to all parts of the world (though often without the spiritual framework) and has become a type of physical exercise and relaxation rather than a spiritual preparation.

Chanting

Chanting is another way of opening the body to increased relaxation and inner peace. Singing is a means of rejoicing in most cultures. This may be related to the fact that people breathe more when they sing. Indeed, for a person whose normal breathing pattern is insufficient, singing can be a useful exercise. In India chanting is a way to reach a higher state of consciousness. The words are often mantras or praises to gods and deities. The melody is often rhythmical with a short tune that is sung repeatedly. During religious celebrations chanting can continue uninterrupted for hours.

The Sanskrit symbol for Om — the original sound of the creation of the universe. It is repeated frequently in many mantras.

The concept of life energy in India

Some concepts in yoga are the same as in qigong, but have no equivalent in the West. The eastern cultures share a common worldview based on subjective observations from inner experiences in meditation. This level of awareness is new to the West. Here it has been modern physics that has led the way to a new understanding of the microcosmos. Physics has shown us a new world with laws that differ from those regulating the visible material world (such as the possibility for something to be both a wave and a particle at the same time). Before these discoveries, there was no need for western science to consider aspects that were not covered by conventional scientific laws.

The concept in the Indian tradition which corresponds most closely to the Chinese concept of *Qi* is known as *prana*. *Prana* is the Sanskrit word for absolute energy. Prana is perhaps the most important concept in yoga. It is the ground principle of energy; the cosmic life force which permeates every atom in the universe. According to Indian mythology, our universe was formed as a projection of *akasha* (space) through prana. Akasha is the basic material of the universe: prana is the basic energy — the cosmic energy — and together they form everything in the universe.

Modern science confirms the eastern theories of Qi and prana, even if many western scientists do not take these theories seriously. The description of prana corresponds well with what is known about the electromagnetic radiation that forms the basic energy for even the smallest particles, and which occurs as a background radiation throughout our universe. Some scientists are even seriously contemplating the concept of life energy. A Swedish research team argues (completely scientifically) that prana is the only suitable fuel for intergalactic travel since it is available everywhere and constantly renewable.

A person who learns to control prana learns to control both the physical and mental aspect of the total energy both in the universe and in their own body and mind. Everything that happens in the universe, everything we do and think, can (potentially) happen in harmony with the cosmic life force, which means that it happens in the most perfect way, where no energy is consumed, nothing is broken down, or worn out. There is a total openness and balance in the stream of energy on all levels, from the microcosmos to the macrocosmos.

Prana stimulates growth in all living organisms at the level of the smallest cells. It is prana that defines the difference between living things and lifeless things. Everything living requires prana in order to exist. Prana exists everywhere and can be absorbed by the body via the food we eat, via our skin, but above all through breathing — but prana is not the same as oxygen; rather it is prana that gives oxygen its life-giving quality.

Pranayama

Pranayama is the name of the breathing exercises which are a central part of yoga. Pranayama is often translated as 'the science of breath' or 'knowledge of how to control prana.' The word pranayama is a combination of *pra* (the first or original entity), *na* (energy), and *ayama* (expansion or manifestation), meaning together a manifestation of the original energy.

As in qigong, the emphasis is on relaxation, inner physical and mental openness, and total concentration when performing the exercises in order to get the optimal effect. When breathing is done with a relaxed body and mental openness, it is possible to get in touch with the 'inner breathing.' This is a type of 'mental breathing' that makes it possible for the body to absorb a higher concentration of prana from the environment.

Physical balance through the mind

This simple exercise balances the body through the mind. Stand with feet slightly apart. Breathe in and bring the palms of the hands together at chest height as for prayer. Breathe out and bring the hands just above the head, palms still together. Maintain a positive thought. Breathe in and bring the hands, palms still together, all the way above your head. Maintain your positive thought. Breathe out and bring the hands back just above the head. Maintain your thought. Breathe in and bring the hands back to chest height still maintaining your thought. Breathe out and return to the starting position. Repeat the exercise as many times as you like and are comfortable with.

The breathing pattern in pranayama is often slower and deeper than normal breathing. The ideal breathing pattern is open — similar to the open breathing during sleep. Some exercises aim at making the pause between inhale and exhale as long as possible and thus create a state of total physical stillness for as long as possible. The breathing pattern is often divided into four parts; inhalation, retention of air, exhalation and pause. Other breathing exercises suggest a faster breathing pattern than normal in order to substantially oxygenate the blood. This has been shown to have a calming effect on the respiratory system and the sympathetic nervous system.

Breathing exercise to calm the mind

This exercise is aimed at making the breathing more balanced and deeper and to still the mind. Sit on a chair with your feet on the floor and your back straight. Breathe slightly deeper than normal for a few breaths. Breathe out as normal. Breathe in while counting slowly to four. Hold the breath while counting to four. Breathe out while counting to four. Make a pause while counting to four. This way the four parts of the breathing get to be the same length. Repeat this pattern for ten minutes. If you find it difficult to breathe slow enough to allow time to count to four, start with a lower number that you are comfortable with; after practice you can increase the time by counting to a higher number. As always in Eastern exercises, the basic rule is to perform exercises in a comfortable way with regard to the limits of your personal capacity — the rule of thumb is to work to 80 per cent capacity. Instead of 'stretching the limits,' the exercises are repeated often so that the body slowly increases its ability in a safe and balanced way.

Pranayama is a very well-known concept in India. In the *Bhagavad Gita,* one of India's most studied scriptures, we read:

Some offer the inward breath in the outward,
likewise the outward in the inward,
checking the flow of both,
on breath control intent.

Bhagavad Gita, 4:29

In the *Gheranda Samhita,* one of the earliest writings on the effects of pranayama, we can read that:

By Pranayama diseases are cured,
by Pranayama the Sakti (spiritual energy) is awakened,
by Pranayama is obtained the calmness of
mind and exaltation of mental powers, by this, mind becomes
*   full of bliss,*
Verily the practitioner of Pranayama is happy.

Gheranda Samhita, 57

Balancing the breath

Stand with your feet slightly apart and arms slightly stretched from the body in a relaxed and open pose. Exhale and start stretching the arms out and up next time you inhale. Don't make it into an exhausting exercise but simply a light movement. Keep the arms stretched out from the shoulders, palms up, in a welcoming and open gesture. Give your invisible audience a big smile as if you are welcoming the whole world. Keep the arms stretched out for a short moment before letting them drop back to the starting point when you exhale. Repeat the exercise several times until you feel uplifted, balanced and ready to go out and meet the world.

Kundalini is one of the greatest energies.
The whole body of the seeker starts glowing
because of the rising of the Kundalini.
Because of that, unwanted impurities in the body disappear.
The body of the seeker suddenly looks very proportionate
and the eyes look bright and attractive and the eyeballs glow.
Gyaneshwara, Chapter VI, AD 1275

Kundalini

One major purpose of yoga exercises is to increase the body's
ability to absorb life energy and, as a consequence, reach a
higher state of awareness. The yoga practitioner must prepare the body and mind carefully for this. A person is not
ready to fully absorb, and benefit from, the strong force from
the universe until the body's own inner life energy has been
awakened and allowed to flow freely in the body.

During childhood the body's natural life energy circulates
freely throughout the body, but after puberty it retracts and
becomes dormant at the base of the spine. In order not to
damage the body and mind, this circulation has to be re-
opened before a person is ready to increase the intake of life
energy. Hatha yoga and pranayama are carefully designed
techniques aimed at making this transition in the safest possible way. Not until the body and mind have been cleared of
energy blockages and 'impurities' are they ready for this
expansion.

In India the body's latent life energy is called *kundalini*.
The name comes from the Sanskrit word *kundal* (curled
up). Initially it is said to refer to a curl from the highest
creator's hair, but a more common explanation is the comparison with a curled up snake. Kundalini is also known as
the 'serpent power' and is illustrated with a snake curling
three and a half times around a *lingam* (the sacred phallic
symbol representing the god Shiva) inside a *yoni* (a triangle pointing downwards representing the feminine sex and

the goddess Shakti). Shiva is the male cosmic principle and Shakti the original nature or earth and the feminine principle. The kundalini force is the union between Shiva and Shakti that is the origin of all species. The snake also corresponds to the body's two energy-flows *pingala* — the positive right *nadi* (energy channel) that energizes the body, and *ida* — the left negative nadi that relaxes the body. (The western symbol for medicine has its origin in this symbol, representing the staff of Asklepios, the Greek demi-god of healing.)

The reason for the sexual connection in the symbol is that the kundalini force is closely linked with the driving force behind sexual activity. In this sense the kundalini force is linked with the absolute point zero of the human body — the conception. The cells that form new life have a unique position representing immortality. They escape death by being transferred from the body to merge with another cell, thus forming new life in an endless chain.

When the life energy is activated, it often leads to physical changes such as decreased need for sleep and food, increased physical stamina and a considerably increased ability for self-healing. It also leads to an expansion of consciousness that can lead to 'supernatural' phenomena (ESP). The change can be immediate, or may take several years.

People who have instantaneous kundalini experiences have often triggered a spontaneous opening in the inner energy flow. This is most likely to occur in critical situations that may lead to a state of physical or psychological shock, though it can also be triggered by intense meditation or similar exercises. Another common cause in the West is the use of recreational drugs that can lead to intense changes of awareness in people who are totally unprepared. The lack of knowledge in this area in western medicine can unfortunately result in long and difficult treatment — something that with the right knowledge could be avoided completely.

The American psychiatrist Lee Sanella gives the following account of the activation of kundalini:

In a darkened room a man sits alone. His body is swept by muscular spasms. Indescribable sensations and sharp pains run from his feet up his legs and over his back and neck. Inside his head he hears roaring sounds and high-pitched whistling. Then suddenly a sunburst floods his inner being. His hands burn. He feels his body tearing within. Then he laughs and is overcome with bliss.[13]

Below are listed and described some of the more common reactions to kundalini awakening, from physical sensations to 'supernatural' phenomena. They are not listed in any specific order, and vary widely from person to person.

Breathing

It is very common for the breathing pattern to change. It may be rapid, shallow breathing or deep powerful breathing. A physiological explanation is that the hypothalamus is affected and controls the blood and oxygenation by controlling the breathing impulse.

Body movements

The body starts to move spontaneously. The movements vary greatly from person to person. They can be soft, curling, jerking, spastic or vibrating. A physiological explanation is that the cerebellum, the part of the brain that coordinates muscular movement, is affected.

Cramps

Various states of cramp occur, affecting all parts of the body. They can last for a short period or persist over a longer time, affecting mobility. States of cramp are normally a reaction to fear or hysteria rather than a direct result of the kundalini experience.

Body sensations

The skin, or the whole body, is felt to vibrate or itch. It is sometimes described as 'bubbles' in the body and can be perceived as sexual, similar to pre-orgasmic feelings. The vibration sensation can move from the feet upwards (the way the kundalini is said to move through the body). The left big toe is often the starting point. This toe has a direct link with the cerebral cortex. (The big toes play a special role in yoga exercises: Hindu mythology also states that the holy river Ganges emerged out of the big toe of the Creator.) A physiological explanation is that the tingling is mainly caused by stimulation of the sensory cortex.

Changes in temperature

The body temperature can rapidly change from very hot to very cold. Sometimes this is a purely subjective experience but there may also be measurable changes. A possible explanation is that when the kundalini force encounters a psychophysical blockage, friction is generated leading to localized temperature rise. This affects the hypothalamus which, in turn, will have effects on body temperature as a whole, causing rapid changes.

Light and sound sensations

There are many descriptions of a wide range of light and sound experiences: colours flowing freely, illuminating or flowing from various parts of the body; voices, music, whistling or strong roaring or hissing. These phenomena may be caused by wave movements in the ventricles (cavities of the brain). This area influences the auditory cortex in the back lobe of the brain, which controls hearing and vision.

Experience of pain

Sudden pain may be felt in the head, eyes, spine or other parts of the body without apparent reason. The pain usually remains for only short periods. A traditional explanation is that the kundalini force becomes intensively concentrated when passing through a 'blocked' part of the body. People who unconsciously try to resist and/or control the experience are likely to experience more pain.

Emotional reactions

Most emotions are experienced as stronger than usual. They can be very intense, ranging from anxiety, fear, hate, depression and confusion, to states of total bliss. Initially negative experiences can be replaced by feelings of peace, harmony and love. A physiological explanation is that the thalamus is affected and causes the intense emotions. This area transports information to various centres in the cortex, in cooperation with the reticular and limbic systems. The latter has great impact on emotions and motivation.

Thoughts

The thought process itself may change. Thoughts pass through the mind faster or slower than usual and thought can even stop completely at times. Thoughts can also appear irrational, strange or unbalanced in states that can resemble mental illness, trance, impulsive actions or confusion.

Distancing

A feeling of separation from the actual event may occur as if it were happening to somebody else. It can also be described as being outside, observing the events, thoughts and feelings. In yoga this is known as 'witness consciousness.' In cases where there is an underlying imbalance in the person, this state may resemble schizophrenia. With the right type of guidance, it usually disappears rapidly and completely.

Out of body experiences

The body may be experienced as larger than usual. The body may appear distant or there may be a feeling of being outside the body. The person can experience moving to various places while leaving the body behind. There is a sharp distinction between this type of experience and ordinary dreaming. The person can actually 'see' their own body from the outside, and is able to describe places without having physically been there, which distinguishes the phenomenon from dreaming or visualization.

Supernatural experiences

In particular in the latter stages of the process of awakening the kundalini force, a capacity for 'supernatural' skills may appear. The most commonly occurring skills are clairvoyance, clairaudience and the ability to see the aura (the body's energy field) but other even more remarkable skills may develop. (For westerners in particular it may seem attractive to develop skills like these; in the East, however, it is regarded as a form of 'spiritual materialism' that a true spiritual seeker must learn to ignore.)

> *All too often people come to meditation in the hope of*
>   *extraordinary results,*
> *like visions, lights, or some supernatural miracle.*
> *When no such thing occurs, they feel extremely disappointed.*
> *But the real miracle of meditation is more ordinary and much*
>   *more useful.*
>   Sogyal Rinpoche, contemporary Tibetan master

The role of breathwork in Tibet

The major religion in Tibet is Buddhism. Here too there are ancient traditions for the use of breathwork, both for spiritual advancement and physical wellbeing. As in the other major Asian cultures, traditionally there is no separation between medical care and religious pursuit. Instead there is a distinction between three aspects for human existence: *Tantra* that represents the cleansing of the body and mind; *the somatic aspect* that represents medicine; and *Dharma*, that represents the religious aspect.

The basic theories regarding life energy have the same origin as in India and China, and most exercises are aimed at achieving the same results in all these cultures. But in Tibet there are also a number of advanced breathing exercises designed for coping with the country's harsh climate. One is aimed at raising the body temperature, and is so efficient that a person can sit naked in the snow without being affected by the cold. Another is designed to ease movement in the road-less and mountainous countryside, by allowing a person to walk much faster than normal. This exercise helps the person to develop a walking technique that is a form of levitation and makes them almost hover over the ground at very high speed.

As one aspect of life energy, the Tibetans also identify *thig-le* which literally means 'creative potential or essence.' It stands for 'blocked wisdom,' that is wisdom that for some reason has been blocked and as a consequence acts in a neg-ative or limiting way. When *thig-le* is released, this means that blocked wisdom is released. This transforms the block-age into a very positive force. It becomes the essence of wis-dom and the source of life energy.

> *May the Being of the Universe*
> *Breathe into you the light of blessing and ripeness*
> *The fulfilment of health and balance*
> Text from the Qumran community 100 BC – AD 100

The role of breathwork in other cultures

It is not just the eastern cultures that recognize a powerful inner life force. Most cultures — from Christian to Islamic mystics (*Sufis*) and various indigenous people have similar concepts. The knowledge and use of breathwork is also is common in most historic cultures.

Greece

In ancient Greece, shamans or medicine men carried out breathing exercises as part of their rituals. Many stories from both Egyptian and Greek mythology are about awakening forces that are linked with the inner life energy. Among oth-ers, the story about Orpheus is said to be based on shamanic rituals. Pythagoras, better known for his mathematical skills, is said to have used mind-altering methods, and Aristotle based his scientific school on *pneuma*, which is the Greek equivalent of life energy that translates as 'cosmic breathing.'

The earliest Greek philosophers argued that everything was alive: hence there were no words to describe matter, since there was no distinction between matter and non-matter. The word *physics* originates from the Greek word *physis* which means 'the real nature of things.' Everything was seen as a manifestation of *physis*. Both *physis* and the human body received their power from *pneuma*, which — in the sense of the body's essence — had a significant role for physical and mental wellbeing, and was introduced to the body from a larger heavenly force. The thought that *pneuma*, or a special force, controlled the brain and all human life remained throughout the historic Greek era. The physician philosopher Claudius Galen (first century AD) developed Aristotle's theories further, and described openings in the arteries close to the skin through which *pneuma* could flow to permeate the body and heart.

Egypt

The ancient Greek and Egyptian cultures had much in common. For the Egyptians the goal was to live in union with *maat*, that is in divine order and harmony. *Maat* is similar to the Chinese concept of Tao which means the divine or right way. The mythology explained how a person should live in order to get in touch with higher forces. Above all, Isis, the Egyptian version of the earth mother, stood for the inner life force. She also has the curled up snake as her special symbol. The goddess Isis and the god Osiris are the Egyptian equivalents of India's Shiva and Shakti that together formed all life on earth.

In Egypt it was the temple priests and magicians who performed breathing exercises and rituals to reach altered states of consciousness. Some advanced initiation rituals demanded that a person was buried alive for a period of time, to pass over to the realm of the dead and become one with the divine sun, before they were re-born to a new and higher spiritual awareness. Some experts argue that the pyramids were built to facilitate this type of spiritual ritual. Some of the ancient knowledge has remained alive with the Egyptian sorcerers who still practice their profession in Egypt.

> *Whosoever knows him-her self, knows the One Self*
>   Literal translation of the word Allah, Neil Douglas-Klotz

Islamic cultures

Dhikr is a form of Islamic breathing exercise, performed mainly by the Sufis — the Islamic mystics. It has many similarities with yoga. The breathing exercises are often performed together with a mantra (a word or phrase with a spiritually uplifting meaning), with which the breathing pattern is coordinated. The best known breathing exercises are probably the whirling dances that the Dervishes (the Islamic monks) perform.

The understanding of the body is traditionally divided into various sections in relation to the psyche. An area beneath the navel is known as 'the most hidden'; an area in the brain is referred to as 'the logic.' There is also a divide between expanded consciousness — *hal* — and the ability to integrate this state of consciousness into ordinary awareness — *makam*. In both Sufism and the Hebrew mystic tradition *Kabbala* there is a connection between breathing and *ruh* (*ruach* in Hebrew) which refers to the spiritual soul. *Ruh* is slightly different to the more down-to-earth 'ego-soul,' and reflects the heaven in a kind of wave-like reality that is closely linked with the breath. There is also a distinction between the inner psychological process where a person's various characteristics are expressed in *Hokhmah* (which can be translated as 'taking care of the breath from below and inside'). This can be described as a form of holy mind or wisdom. This concept is also found in the Greek culture under the name *Sophia*.

Oh Breathing life, your name shines everywhere
Release a space to plant your presence — here
Envision your 'I can' now
Embody your desire in every light and form
Grow through us, this moment's bread and wisdom
Untie the knots that failure brings us
As we release the strands we hold of others' faults
Help us not forget our source
Yet free us from not being in the present

The Lord's Prayer, retranslated from the original
Aramaic by Neil Douglas-Klotz

Christian cultures

Neil Douglas-Klotz has retranslated texts from the Bible from the original Aramaic versions.[14] He claims that there are a number of references to the use of the breath that have been mistranslated in the Greek version, which subsequently formed the original source for most other language translations. In fact, he argues that the mistranslations are so many and severe that they should be regarded more as interpretations of the original texts than literal translations. One example is the Aramaic word for spirit that also means breath, air and wind. In addition, the Aramaic language lacks prepositions indicating 'inner' and 'outer,' 'within' and 'among,' which gives alternative translations of concepts such as 'the heavenly realm.' In the original texts it is indicated that Jesus was well aware of the power of the breath and used it when he performed his healing.

When Christianity started to spread in Europe, a group of Greek Christian monks called the *Hesychasts* (quietists) practised a meditative form of worship that involved an elaborate system of asceticism. Their name originates from the Greek word *hesychia* that means 'stillness' or 'inner silence.' According to the Hesychasts, words, images, and thoughts were a limited experience of God. Their goal was to free the mind and open up to God's full expression — the 'uncreated light of God' (which is said to be the same light that appeared at Christ's transfiguration). They distinguished between God's essence and God's energy (activity in the world). Since it was impossible to know God in person, it was God's energy that came through in prayer. To really experience God's energy, breathing exercises were performed, aimed at slowing the breathing and consequently the mind. Part of this exercise is to press the chin against the breath and hold the breath, eyes turned in, until a wonderful light appears. Their experience of increased energy and mental clarity was so strong that it could only come directly from God.

A collection of early Christian writings compiled by Nicodemus Hagioretes gives the following instructions:

> Then sit down in a quiet cell, in a corner by yourself, and do what I tell you. Close the door, and withdraw your intellect from everything worthless and transient. Rest your beard on your chest, and focus your physical gaze, together with the whole of your intellect, upon the centre of your belly or your navel. Restrain the drawing-in of breath through your nostrils, so as not to breathe easily, and search inside yourself with your intellect so as to find the place of the heart, where all the powers of the soul reside. To start with you will find there darkness and an impenetrable density. Later, when you persist and practice this task day and night, you will find, as though miraculously, an unceasing joy. For as soon as the intellect attains the place of the heart, at once it sees things of which it previously knew nothing. It sees the open space within the heart and it beholds itself entirely luminous and full of discrimination.[15]

The Greek monks on the mountain island of Athos have known about, and used, breathwork for centuries. The religious text *Enchiridion* argues that the mind should be stilled during prayer, since the mind — or the actions of the mind —

are accustomed from childhood to dissolve and spread among everyday events.

> When you utter this prayer you should not breathe consistently, as nature demands, but hold the breath slightly until the inner world once has uttered the prayer ... by holding the breath this short moment, the hard and cold heart gets thin and when the humbleness of the heart has been sufficiently warmed it will become softer, more sensitive and humble and more prone to release negativity and cry more freely.

Later on in Europe there are several accounts of Christian mystics and deeply religious people with experiences of awakening an inner life force. These were often a consequence of intensive prayers, periods of fasting or ascetic practices. The reports are often about young women who describe the experience as fights with the devil, or intensive experiences of Christ or God. The symptoms include inexplicable illnesses with high fever, shivering, cramps, spasms, hallucinations, even temporary insanity. The illness usually lasted only a short period and disappeared as quickly and inexplicably as it appeared.

A Swedish book published in the fourteenth century tells the story of a young woman's religious quest — the blessed maiden Kristina of Stommeln. She had many religious experiences with strong physical and psychological reactions. One passage has an extended account of such an experience:

> When she had been sitting like this, slightly leaned forward on the bench, with her face and hands covered by a veil, for about three or four hours, she suddenly sighed, so that the body was put into a light movement. She slowly began to breathe, though slower and lighter than people usually breathe. Her breathing was so slow and unusual that only with the outmost attention could it be noticed. She took, as I said, a breath in much quieter and lighter way than normal, but the time that

elapsed between inhalation and exhalation was, in spite of this (which seems contradictory), much longer than usual. When she had been sitting like this for about the time required for two masses, she gradually began to breathe deeper in a conventional way. Then she started talking, but still so softly that it could hardly be discerned by the most perceptive listener and not in coherent sentences, but with disconnected phrases, pet names and love words such as 'you highly beloved,' 'the most precious,' 'my most beloved,' 'darling,' and 'bridegroom,' seeming to rejoice with mysterious shivering, so that her whole body shivered and remained in this shivering rejoice longer than a Miserere, all this in one and the same breath, whereby she again became immobile, though not for as long. This state of laughter, shivering, bliss and joy — I don't know how to describe it, since I have never seen anything like it before — lasted, I think, as long a time as two masses. Her onlookers were brought to tears through the incredible holiness and burning love, which she hereby gave multiplied expression to.[16]

The Swedish scientist and philosopher Emmanuel Swedenborg, discovered the power of the breath as a young child. Without any knowledge of yoga he developed his own breathing technique that has much in common with pranayama. Later in life he had several mystical experiences, which he described in detail in many of his books. His conclusion was that humans have two kinds of breathing, one physical and one spiritual. These two breaths can be separated or united. In ordinary people, in particular in charlatans they are separated, but rarely in spiritual or serious people.

Take the breath of the new dawn and make it part of yours. It will give you strength.

Hopi Saying

Tribal societies

Breathwork is still used in some tribal societies as a way to reach states that resembles awakening of life energy. The *!Kung* people from the Kalahari desert, who are said to have 'supernatural powers' live today as they have done for thousands of years and are a living example of how all humans lived in prehistoric times. The men of the !Kung tribe dance for hours to 'warm up *n/um*' as a preparation for the state of *!kia*. N/um greatly resembles kundalini. !Kia is a transcendental state. Everyone who experiences *n/um and !kia* will automatically become n/um masters. A rich imagination and emotional openness are useful attributes for becoming a *n/um* master. Some tribe members find it easier to reach a trance state than others. Above all the older men can reach trance almost at will. Even if the dance starts spontaneously women never participate. They remain sitting in a ring around the men, clapping and encouraging the dance. A member of the tribe describes the role of the breathing in this ritual:

> You dance, dance, dance, dance. The *n/um* lifts you in the belly and lifts you in the back, and then you start to shiver. N/um makes you tremble — it is hot. Your eyes are open but you don't look around; you hold your eyes still and look straight ahead. But when you get into *!kia*, you are looking around because you see everything, because you see what is troubling everybody ... Rapid shallow breathing — that's what draws *n/um* ... then *n/um* enters every part of the body, right to the tip of your feet and even your hair.

Another member of the tribe says:

> In your backbone you feel a pointed something and it works its way up. Then the base of your spine is tingling, tingling, tingling, tingling, tingling, tingling, tingling ... and it makes your thoughts nothing in your head.[17]

A visiting westerner presents this picture:

> At first the rhythm is restrained, but one can sense the enormous tension, as if a flood of energy is being held back tightly controlled ... One feels the power of millennia past, reaching out to tug gently at the soul and strange responses start from within ... To them, the trance world is real, and survival in the living world is dependent upon successful communication with the non-living world.[18]

Given the large number of scientific studies of the !Kung tribe it is possible to provide medical explanations as to why the trance occurs through the dancing:

> Hours of energetic dancing attune every muscle to the rhythm, and there is an exact and monotonous balance between demand and supply of oxygen. In order to induce a state of trance, the dancer shortens his breathing, without reducing the level of his physical exertions. An oxygen deficiency is created which leads to drowsiness and profuse sweating. The heart pumps more strongly in order to circulate the blood through the lungs more rapidly and, at the same time, blood pressure in the brain is increased.[19]

According to the Micronesian Sabarl people, *binona* is essential for the birth of a child: *binona* is the same as the essence of life that makes the body breathe. The Laboya people believe that the newborn baby's soul has different parts that must be brought together so that *mawo* — the breath and life force — does not become restless and leave the body. The Malay people say that the newborn baby's energy consists of *ruh* — soul, *nyawa* — the breath of life, and *semangat* — the spirit of life, while the soul of a dying person escapes through the nostrils. In Thailand, the *tham khwam* tradition is to tie the life force or soul to the baby's body with unspun cotton.

Among the aboriginal inhabitants of Greenland two different sources of the human soul are identified: one is the person's shadow; the other is the person's breath. A Nicaraguan tradition which was recorded in 1528 gives an explanation of what happens at the moment of death:

> When they die, there comes out of their mouth something that resembles a person and is called *julio* (from the Aztec word *yuli,* to live). This being goes to the place where the man and woman are. It is like a person but does not die and the body remains here.[20]

If there is a 'royal way' (to the unconscious) it may consist of deep breathing. Deep breathing techniques, in combination with other methods can, for some patients, contribute to loosing up the immense power of the pain inside the body.

Arthur Janov

Modern breathing techniques

Over the last several hundred years there has been a steady decline in the wider use of the breath in the western world. Breathing was gradually reduced to its physiological function, with very little interest and knowledge of its wider potential. During the last century this trend started to change. This renewed interest has been mainly in techniques which follow eastern traditions.

One of the first westerners to show an interest in the wider potential of the breath was the Frenchman François Delsarte (1811–71). During the second half of the nineteenth century he studied the connection between song and dance and the body's natural movements and functions. As a result, he developed a number of breathing techniques aimed at improving flexibility, in both the voice and the body. Delsarte's training programme spread to America and back to Europe where Elsa Gindler, one of Germany's best known gymnastics teachers at the time, developed her own breathing exercises from Delsarte's methods. Gindler's techniques were based on a higher awareness of the body's functions rather than a mechanical approach. The Austrian organist and choir leader Leo Kofler, born in 1837, was another contemporary developer of new breathing exercises. His goal was to improve the vocal qualities of his choir singers at St Paul's church in New York. His teaching contributed to formation of the Rotenburgian breathwork school that still is active in Germany. Following this reawakening of interest in breathing techniques, a number of western breathwork schools have emerged, many aimed at re-training patients suffering from breathing disorders.

Every muscular rigidity contains the history and meaning of its origin.
                                                    Wilhelm Reich

The role of the breath in modern psychology

Given the focus on the physiological aspects of breathing in western medicine, or rather the lack of insights into the wider potential of the breath, breathing has played an indirect (but still important) role in modern psychology. Although little has been done to use the full potential of the breath, techniques employing it have been used in psychology, mainly in regard to promoting relaxation and making the mind more accessible. And, as the understanding of the mind has increased in the western world, breathing techniques have come to play a more and more important role in psychotherapy.

Sigmund Freud (1856–1939)

It would be wrong to claim that Freud gave breathing a special significance, but as the founder of modern psychology he has been important for the theoretical framework behind modern breathing techniques. To begin with Freud used hypnosis (where breathing plays an important part) and suggestion as tools in his treatments. When he gradually developed his theory of the role of the unconscious mind, he focused mainly on psychoanalysis. He based his work and his understanding of the human mind on experiments he made when he studied hypnosis with the famous French professor in neurology Jean-Martin Charcot. Hysteria was a central concept for Charcot, who described this as a condition that could lead to paralysis and epileptic seizures. Contrary to previous views that hysteria had a physiological cause, Freud soon realized that hysteria could also be provoked through hypnosis.

According to yoga teaching the shape of the nose is important for how the body is supplied with energy, which may affect the mind. Freud too saw a close link between the nose and the mind. (One reason may have been his close friendship with the German nose specialist Wilhelm Vlies.) One of Freud's better known cases was a woman patient who suffered constant headaches after a nose operation. Freud's conclusion was that she suffered from psychological trauma that he tried to treat with psychotherapy, without much success. It was later discovered that the real cause of the headaches in effect was a piece of tissue that had been left in her nose during the operation.

Some modern nose specialists also argue that the shape of the nose has vital importance both psychologically and physically and that surgery in this area can lead to psychological problems. This means that there may be a less known side effect of cosmetic plastic surgery (a form of surgery that is becoming more and more popular).

Carl Gustav Jung (1875–1961)

Freud's student Carl Jung, who was another important influence on modern psychology, probably cared even less about the role of breathing than Freud, since he was criticized for paying too little attention to the body as a whole. Still Jung showed a great interest in the altered states of consciousness that often are a result of breathwork and contributed widely to the western understanding of the unconscious mind.

Jung's major contribution was to divide the unconscious into a personal aspect and archetypes — our commonly shared symbolic images that date back a long way in human history. Jung's archetypal world is a domain between everyday reality and a higher awareness that is part of the shared human unconscious. Experiences in this realm are not generated in the ordinary senses and can only be experienced in non-ordinary states of mind. In this realm it is possible to experience mythical beings in a way that gives a completely different sense of time and space. It is a dream-like state that is possible to reach even outside ordinary dreams. Entering into this reality seems to have unusually strong energy and give a sense of being some kind of godlike creature.

For Jung, the most important factor was to reach harmony between the conscious and unconscious mind, since it is that harmony which makes a person whole. He believed that people should analyse their daily activities in a systematic self-exploration. By turning inwards, we may be able to get in touch with our higher selves, and get direct guidance from the common unconscious world that contains all the wisdom humankind has built up since time immemorial. Only by utilizing experiences from the outer material world together with the deeper wisdom inside ourselves, are we able to form the right decisions in life.

Otto Rank (1884–1939)

Another of Freud's students, Otto Rank, has contributed most significantly with a cartography of the psyche that led to a wider understanding of the effects of breathwork that are linked with how we are influenced by our own birth trauma (that we will examine in more detail later). Rank's theories around the relationship between mother and child clearly deviated from Freud's more male-oriented theories, and were heavily criticized by the Freudian school. Rank distanced himself from the process of psychoanalysis, and together with Sandor Frenczi he developed a more egalitarian and active form of psychotherapy with a greater focus on the present situation — the 'here and now.' This focused on real relationships, conscious mind and will, rather than past experiences, transference between patient and therapist, and unconscious and hidden desires. This approach has influenced the client/therapist relationship in modern breathwork techniques.

Fritz Perls (1893–1970)

Another contributor to the theoretical framework for modern breathwork techniques is Fritz Perls. His main contribution to modern psychology was to realize the importance of acting out emotions. After his training as a psychoanalyst in Berlin and Austria he developed the *Gestalt* therapy. Perls' theories emphasise a phenomenological and subjective approach to therapy. He noted that many people distance themselves from experiences, emotions and thoughts that they experience as uncomfortable. One of Perls' goals was to move people to own their own experiences and to develop a healthy *Gestalt* (or whole).

> *All our patients report that they went through periods in their childhood in which, by means of certain practices in vegetative behaviour (holding the breath, tensing the abdominal muscular pressure, etc.), they learned to suppress their impulses of hate, anxiety, and love ...* It is precisely the physiological process of repression *that deserves our keenest attention.*
>
> Wilhelm Reich

One of the first figures in modern psychology to significantly emphasise the role of the breath was Wilhelm Reich. According to his theories the body forms a rigid muscular armour, in particular around the chest restricting breathing and thereby blocking emotional expression. He also argued that human emotions are reflected in different parts of the body. He noted that when a person does not want to recognize a certain emotion the body assumes a defensive posture. The muscles are tightened and the breathing becomes shorter and more shallow, thus preventing the emotion from reaching consciousness. When such a defensive posture is kept for extended periods of time it becomes chronic and the muscles become locked into a rigid 'shield' or 'armour.' Only physical manipulation (via massage or pressure) can dissolve this armour and return the muscles to a normal condition.

Reich assumed that the personality consists of several layers corresponding to different periods and events in a person's life. Experiences from childhood form the inner layers whereas impressions from later periods in life appear closer to the surface. He argued that children quickly learn to suppress impulses in order to fit in with their environment and become accepted as members of their society.

Reich named his body-oriented therapy Vegetotherapy. It was aimed at softening the body armour with the help of pressure or massage so that the vegetative functions (digestion, breathing and sexual orgasm), could be fully released. When tensions are sufficiently released, memories from childhood can surface and be acted out. Vegetotherapy includes breathing exercises aimed at reducing the energy level and thereby keeping anxiety under control.

Vegetotherapy consists of seven main parts: Deep breathing and screaming or making faces, deep tissue massage, applying pressure on the patient's chest while they are screaming, paying attention to reflexes to cough, vomit and yawn, exhausting body postures and bio-energetic movements.

Reich soon realized that breathing is more than the intake of vital oxygen. It is also an intake of another kind of energy. He became convinced that this was a real, physical energy flow and that it caused the liberating changes in Vegetotherapy. Having studied with Freud, Reich remained loyal to the theory that sexuality plays an important role for our psychological wellbeing. He concluded that the body energy he had identified was closely linked with the sexual drive. He named it *orgone* energy (from the words organism and orgasm) and argued that it is present everywhere in the universe. He saw human beings as manifestations of this pulsating energy and the personality and muscle armour as defences against it. Disruptions in this energy, he argued, can cause illness.

Reich built various instruments to measure the energy generated by the body, and found that humans generate large amounts of electrical energy during the sexual orgasm. From this he concluded that the energy formed during orgasm is of great importance for our wellbeing.

Reich came to believe that orgone energy was the beginning of all life and made several attempts to create new life using orgone energy in concentrated form in a totally sterile environment. He also built a special box that he called the orgone accumulator. In it he exposed his patients to concentrated orgone energy, which he claimed had a healing and life-giving effect and some of his cancer patients also reacted positively to this treatment. This part of Reich's research was however exposed to severe criticism from medical and psychological professionals. During the 1950s he was subject to legal prosecution and sentenced to prison where he later died.

Despite the many obvious similarities, Reich never made any connection between his theories and eastern philosophies of life energy. Instead he formed his own theoretical framework. He was the first psychotherapist to develop a treatment which involved the whole body as well as the breath, emotional catharsis and integration of re-experienced memories and is regarded by many as the founder of body-oriented or bio-functional psychotherapies.

> *'Let it happen ... feel the energy in the hand ... see how it feels ... go with the movement.' The essence of this work is the energetic process; to liberate the repressed energy and help it to become integrated in the client's circulation and consciousness.*
>
> Southwell

Body psychotherapy

Since the 1970s a number of psychotherapeutic schools have emerged which feature a more focused use of the breath. They are commonly known as body psychotherapy. The breathing techniques and their use vary between different schools. They are mainly used in combination with other forms of psychotherapy. According to the body psychotherapist Tree Staunton:

> ... the fundamental premise in body psychotherapy is that our *core beliefs are embodied,* and that until

we begin to experience the pain held in them *directly through our bodies* they will continue to run our lives, even if we mentally understand them.[21]

The body psychotherapist Nick Totton argues that:

> The central focus of embodied-relational bodywork, then, is on re-establishing a fuller, more spontaneous breath — not by efforting, but by gradually letting go of our need to protect ourselves from feeling by not breathing. Working systematically through all the levels of resistance to spontaneous breath — to 'being breathed' — therapist and client encounter all the familiar relationship issues that emerge through free association, or indeed any other sustained encouragement to let things happen spontaneously and without censorship.[22]

The Buteyko method

One of the new breathing methods which is attracting growing recognition, is the Buteyko method, developed by the Russian Konstantin Pavlovich Buteyko. It is a drug free method of treating asthma and other breathing disorders entirely based on breathing exercises. These are aimed at improving the overall quality of the breathing. According to Buteyko, too many westerners suffer from insufficient breathing and need to re-learn their natural breathing pattern. The method has been tried and evaluated in a number of countries with positive results. In particular asthma patients have been able to reduce their medicine intake substantially. Part of the technique involves learning to hold the breath for long periods. It is claimed that this has a particularly positive psychological effect on asthma suffers, given that a contributing negative factor in asthma is the psychological stress the patient experiences when not able to breathe sufficiently. The idea is that learning to hold the breath for long periods gives suffers a sense of control when subject to an attack.

Buteyko breathing test

Since this test is aimed at detecting potential breathing disorders, please be extra careful and stop at the slightest sign of discomfort.

Take ten deep breaths. Notice how this feels. Do you feel like coughing? Do you get dizzy? If not take another ten deep breaths. Notice how this feels. Does your chest feel restricted?

If this short exercise has given you any discomfort it may indicate that you would benefit from thorough assessment of your breathing.

The Buteyko method's carbon dioxide test

Sit on a chair with both feet on the ground. Keep your back straight. Make sure that nothing is restricting your breathing. Breathe normally. Prepare to time yourself and exhale normally. Make a note of the time when you start and wait as long as possible before you inhale again. As soon as you start to feel uncomfortable, check how long you have been holding your breath then return to your normal breathing.

Between 40–60 seconds without breathing indicates a healthy breathing pattern. 30 seconds mean that you breathe twice as often as you ought to. This indicates poor breathing although not a breathing disorder. If you can hold your breath for only 20 seconds, you are breathing three times as often as normal. This indicates a mild breathing disorder. If you only counted 10 seconds you may be suffering from chronically poor breathing. And if you only counted five seconds you should definitely seek medical advice to establish whether you are suffering from asthma or some other chronic breathing disorder.

One symptom of insufficient breathing is the constant loss of carbon dioxide. The focus of the Buteyko method is therefore to restore the body's ability to absorb carbon dioxide and to increase the carbon dioxide level in the body. In order to determine the carbon dioxide level patients are tested as to how long they can hold their breath after exhaling. A simple way to measure this is to count how many seconds you can hold your breath.

Extreme breathing forms

The most extreme form of all new breathing techniques is known as Breatharianism. This can be defined as 'the ability to live on air alone.' This technique was developed by an Australian woman now generally known as Jasmuheen. By combining mental exercises and fasting, the body is trained with the aim to survive without food. There are similar yoga exercises, mainly from Tibet, aimed at lowering the body's requirement for food, but these have nothing to do with Breatharianism which is an entirely modern technique.

Approximately five thousand people around the world are said to have learnt to live without food since the 1980s, but so far there have been no independently confirmed cases. Despite several attempts to monitor and verify that a person can survive completely without food for long periods of time, it has not as yet proved possible to achieve this beyond doubt.

A notable western case of dramatically reduced food intake, was a deeply religious German woman called Therese Neumann. After some intense religious experiences, she spontaneously stopped eating and drank very little for several decades, living a very quiet and simple life (despite this, Adolf Hitler apparently became aware of her and regarded her supernatural powers as a great threat.)

Breath is the key to the mystery of life,
to that of the body as well as to that of the spirit.

Lama Anagarika Govinda

The Rebirthing Technique

The hippie movement, during the 1960s and 1970s in America and Europe, led to a widespread experimentation with altered states of consciousness for a whole generation in the western world. This was driven largely by the increased availability and consumption of recreational drugs.

When the first wave of positive drug-induced experiences was past, and people started to seriously acknowledge the downside of increased drug use, many started looking for alternatives. This led to a substantial increase of interest in breathing techniques such as yoga, qigong and other eastern breathwork techniques that led to similar experiences that the drugs offered, but in a healthy and safe way.

A number of modern breathing techniques developed, driven by the same impetus. Some of these have grown over the years and spread to all parts of the world. Two of the most successful, both developed in the USA during the 1970s, are Rebirthing, mainly developed by Leonard Orr, and Holotropic Breathwork developed by Stanislav and Christina Grof, which is described in more detail below. Of the two, Rebirthing has done the most to develop a specific technique, with the aim of achieving very subtle, but efficient, differences in the breathing pattern so as to influence both body and mind. Holotropic Breathwork uses a combination of breathing and music to achieve similar results.

The Rebirthing technique was developed in California in the 1970s by Leonard Orr. Orr, with no formal background in psychology, developed the technique as part of his wider search for 'self-improving methods' in which he exposed himself to varying elements and conditions: for example, he underwent long sessions in hot saunas, or submerged in warm water, simply to see what effects this would have on his body and mind. He soon discovered that some situations led to strong emotional reactions, and triggered memories of what he considered were traumatic situations he had experienced earlier in his life. He also noticed that his breathing pattern changed spontaneously when he had these emotional reactions. Orr continued to experiment with different breathing patterns to see if he could deliberately trigger similar reactions, and found that it worked very well. The effect was even more intense reactions and experiences, and he became convinced that these were memories from his own birth.

As he continued to experiment, he told others about his experiences and started to guide their breathing in similar ways. Orr soon discovered that most people had similar reactions to the changed breathing pattern and triggered memories, with the birth as the strongest experience. As a consequence the method was called *Rebirthing*. Since then it has also been taught under other names, such as *Conscious (Connected) Breathing* or simply *Breathwork*. Among Orr's first group of students were well-known breathwork teachers such as Sondra Ray, Bob Mandel, Jim Leonard, Phil Laut and Jim Morningstar, all of whom developed their own breathwork schools (some under other names such as Vivation).

Here follows Leonard Orr's own account of the first development of Rebirthing from an interview with the author in 1989:

> The ideas about Rebirthing came as a result of personal evolution. My first Rebirthing experience was actually in 1962. I was taking a bath and felt as if I couldn't get out of the bath. Of course I didn't understand what it was all about until years later. I had many 'bathtub' experiences like that between 1962 and 1968, but in 1968 I started having conscious birth memories when I was in my bathtub. And of course, in the years 1965 to 1967, I unravelled my 'death-urge.' *[Author. A special concept introduced by Orr, similar to Freud's theory of an unconscious death-wish influencing the psyche.]* This gave me a totally safe place in my mind and I

felt safe in the physical universe. That safety enabled me to have more conscious memories of my birth.

The immortal energy has always been the basis of Rebirthing energy. It is no secret that rebirthers who have actually unravelled their death-urge and their birth-trauma produce very different benefits for their clients than rebirthers who are just breath-technicians. In a certain sense even expert breathing guides don't have the same depth to their intuition as rebirthers who have unravelled the birth-death cycle or at least a significant part of it.

The next development was a seminar I held in 1974 where I described my experiences of remembering my birth. The people there said they too wanted to have those kinds of experiences. So I suggested that they should get into their bathtubs and stay there until they felt they should get out. After that they should stay at least half an hour or an hour longer. There is a natural urgency barrier in the mind that keeps us from going too deep into ourselves. When people relax through that urgency barrier they have fantastic realizations about themselves. These people from the seminar had such powerful and dramatic experiences that they wanted me to be present when they were going through them. That is where the idea of the rebirther came from. After watching a couple of people, I got the idea of using a snorkel and nose-clip in a big hot-tub, so that a couple of people could be in the water at the same time.

That is how Rebirthing really started. Guiding several hundred Rebirthing experiences, I noticed that people had a transformation of their breathing mechanism which I called 'the healing of the breath.' I wondered if it was possible to guide people into the breathing rhythm that I saw spontaneously during these experiences. I experimented and found that it was.[23]

To begin with, the breathing sessions were done in hot water, with the person either lying face down, breathing through a snorkel or floating on their back. Since the focus was on recreating the birth situation, people would also stay in a sleeping bag for up to 14 hours to re-enact the birth situation as effectively as possible. The water sessions often led to such strong emotional reactions that they had to be completed out of the water. This was the beginning of the 'dry sessions' that gave the same experiences, but in a calmer way. It also became apparent that the strong emotional reactions were gradually replaced with calmer reactions. Once a person could interpret and understand the underlying meaning behind an experience, it was as though it automatically became less dramatic. Sometimes a particular memory would recur several times and lead to several insights before it finally dissolved.

The Rebirthing breathing pattern

In contrast to many eastern techniques, the Rebirthing technique focuses entirely on the breath without body movements. Usually the breathing session is done lying down and the body movements that may occur are totally spontaneous and uncontrolled. (Lying down helps to free the parts of the brain that control body movements, which are said to stimulate experiences of altered states of consciousness.) Briefly the technique can be described as a relaxed, connected and total breathing pattern. It is not very different from the ordinary breathing pattern of a relaxed person, and very similar to the deep breathing pattern during relaxed sleep. The breathing is as open and unrestricted as in very young children or animals, in a stress-free environment.

The main difference between Rebirthing and normal breathing is that there is no pause between inhale and exhale and that the pattern is more rhythmical than normal. In normal breathing there is usually a tiny pause between inhale and exhale. This pause may act as a kind of inner balancing of the mind that helps maintain awareness of everyday reality. By deliberately removing this pause and breathing out immediately after each inhale, the mind is affected in a way it is not familiar with.

The other important element is that the exhale is totally relaxed. The air is simply transported out of the body when the diaphragm and the intercostal muscles relax. When the chest cavity gets smaller as a result of this, the air has only one place to go — which is out the same way it came in. (A good comparison is a wave that moves evenly on a sandy beach. The water moves in with some force, and moves out again totally without resistance, as the sand level sinks away.) Normally we only use this breathing pattern when we are totally relaxed. As soon as there is any element of stress or increased activity, the body reacts by contracting the muscles around the breathing apparatus in order to control and limit the breathing. Together with the pause between inhale and exhale, this is said to be our main way of remaining in everyday reality and staying aware of what happens around us.

This is how Leonard Orr explains it:

> The most important part is merging the inhale to the exhale. When you merge the inhale to the exhale you are experiencing the unity of being, on the physiological level. In a breath you are experiencing the merging of spirit and matter. I call it the biological experience of God.
>
> The connected breathing is the natural form of breathing the spirit into the body. Newborn babies breathe that way. People breathe that way in the middle of deep sleep. That is not to say that there isn't some value in doing some different kind of exercises. I particularly believe in alternated nasal breathing. That is inhaling through one nostril and exhaling through the other in an alternated way. That particular exercise cleanses the passages from the nostrils into the nervous system. When those passages are cleaned, energy is integrated in the

body in a way that heals and maintains all organs.

When I saw people's breathing mechanism being transformed in early Rebirthing sessions I verbalised it as 'learning to breathe from the breath itself.' This is an internal realization for people at a certain point in the process. This experience was not induced in the beginning. It was a spontaneous experience. When I saw it happen I asked myself if it was possible to induce the experience, by guiding a person's breathing rhythm into the rhythm I saw when it occurred spontaneously. I found it was. But when I guided a person's breathing rhythm into the experience of learning from the breath itself, merging the inner breath with the outer breath, the person did not perceive what was happening. That is, they could not learn that breathing rhythm in two or three sessions. But a high percentage of people did learn. They learned the intuitive connection between the inner breath and the outer breath frequently in five to fifteen sessions. So there is a point at which a person notices that they are breathing energy as well as air. When that realization dawns upon the mind and soul of the individual, they have learned to breathe. That is what we mean when we call it conscious breathing. Conscious breathing is to consciously make that connection in the breathing rhythm. You merge the inhale with the exhale. That is the technique, but the power or the spirit of the technique is the intuitive knowledge that you are breathing energy as well as air.[24]

By consciously creating a connected and relaxed breathing pattern, a person can trigger a natural process in the body that has a cleansing and purifying effect, both mentally and physically. Over time this increased mental and physical relaxation increases openness and oxygen intake. This makes it possible to dissolve psycho-physiological blocks that stand in the way of the body's natural circulation. Increased relaxation makes the body's muscles less tense, which improves circulation. This stimulates the body's natural ability for self-healing of psychological and physiological ailments (above all psychosomatic illness). When the healing process has been stimulated the body seems to know exactly what to do to restore health and recharge with new energy. Despite the fact that this process is purely physiological, it does affect the mind as well as the body.

We will examine in more detail later how the increased oxygen level leads to a release of chemicals in the blood stream. These are chemicals that act as transporters of information throughout the body, and when they pass the brain they may be experienced as memories. To block a memory literally means to prevent the circulation in the body through tightening the muscles. The release of blocked memories therefore gives the body an added supply of energy. This can be experienced as a mental sharpening that improves both physical and mental performance.

In Rebirthing the breathing can be done through either the nose or the mouth, but not mixed; but which one you choose makes a difference to the experiences. To breathe through the nose tends to stimulate a mental approach to blocked experiences, whereas mouth-breathing tends to trigger more physical experiences. The experiences can also be influenced by the intensity and speed of the breathing pattern. Short and intensive breathing leads to a physical exhaustion of the breathing apparatus and makes it more difficult to maintain control of the breathing. This pattern is often used to get past emotional blocks. Long and deep breaths help to express emotional reactions that the person would otherwise prefer to express in some form of catharsis.

> ### *Twenty connected breaths*
>
> This is a mini-version of Rebirthing that has a calming effect on the body. It also gives clearer thoughts and calmer emotions.
>
> Sit on a chair with both feet on the ground and a straight back, and make sure your breathing is unrestricted. Take a deep breath and start to breathe in and out as normal, but without any pause at all between inhale and exhale. The exhale is completely relaxed but not deeper than normal. Count to four breaths like this. Make the fifth breath as deep as possible — still without pause — and make sure the exhale is relaxed. Continue with four more connected breaths as before followed by another deep breath. Continue as before until you have done a total of 20 connected breaths. Finish the exercise by returning to normal breathing and sit still for a few moments before you return to everyday life.

Apart from changing the breathing pattern — that is to say the inhale, since the exhale is always completely relaxed — the breath can also be directed to various parts of the body. Breathing in the upper part of the chest tends to activate the upper part of the body, whereas breathing predominantly in the lower part of the chest tends to activate the lower part. By concentrating the attention to a specific area and 'breathing into this area' it is possible to activate memories that may be linked to this specific part of the body. This often works best if the person has had a specific experience in a particular part of the body. It can be pain, irritation or some form of tension or dysfunction in the particular area. Physical signs of this kind are often an indication that memories have been triggered and are 'ready' to be released and integrated.

As with the eastern techniques it is important that the environment is calm and peaceful without disturbances or stimuli. This is so attention can be fully focused inwards. Rebirthing is done best lying on the back, with feet slightly apart and the hands with palms upwards, so that the body is resting without any restriction of the breathing. In yoga this position is called *shavanasa* and is often used in relaxation exercises.

A Rebirthing session usually lasts around one hour, but can take up to three hours. The time is decided by the body's spontaneous reaction to the connected and relaxed breathing pattern. Exactly what determines how long the spontaneous breathing pattern is maintained is not clear, but it corresponds well with the body's natural activity pattern that spans approximately ninety minutes. The most common pattern is that when the connected and relaxed breathing pattern is activated — which can take from one minute to two hours — it will continue for another thirty minutes to one hour.

Despite the early realization of how the body and mind could be influenced by the breath, it did not take long to realize that a Rebirthing session could be done without assistance. In the early days, the guiding rule used to be ten assisted sessions to learn how to do sessions on your own. These days the common view is that even if the majority of people know how much they can deal with without assistance, some people may require extensive help and support for all their sessions. Today the teaching of all reputable schools is also much more extensive.

The general recommendation is that the first sessions are always done with the supervision of an experienced practitioner. This is both to learn the correct breathing pattern, and because the reactions can at first be overwhelming, even frightening for the inexperienced. One of the biggest problems during the first sessions is to maintain an open and relaxed breathing pattern when emotions and memories have been activated. An experienced practitioner knows how to guide the person so that they can maintain the correct pattern. Leonard Orr makes the following comments:

People are so constructed that if you only use the technique of merging the inhale with the exhale, the experience will take place in most people spontaneously. The skill of a good rebirther is determined by their intuition. To be able to see, to hear and to feel the energy merging with the air. Training people in intuition is not possible. In that sense Rebirthing is not a technique. It is an inspiration beyond technique. People can ultimately only learn intuition through inner realization. You can provide an environment for people to learn intuition, and it is possible to observe when a person does develop that intuitive skill but there is no way you can force it.[25]

After the initial period of more or less free experiments to find the best structure for the Rebirthing session, the conclusion was that, given a safe and calm space, it did not matter very much what happened in the surrounding environment — the most important part was the breathing pattern. The water sessions continued, since they tend to trigger different and stronger responses than the dry sessions. A possible explanation for this is that the hot water — slightly over body temperature — triggers memories from the birth, probably because the hot water gives associations to the womb. Similarly, Rebirthing in cold water was subsequently introduced and found to associate to death and fear of death. (Since Rebirthing sessions in water are connected with a certain risk of drowning, they are always conducted with at least one assistant.) Leonard Orr explains:

> There is a big difference between warm and cold water sessions. Warm water stimulates womb memories and deep psycho-analytical and psycho-physiological experiences. It induces a state of very deep relaxation. Our whole physical body was formed in the medium of warm water in the womb. So our basic emotional structure is formed in the medium of hot water. Birth is the first experience of cold. Cold water Rebirthing

has a tendency to dissolve our temperature trauma and other unpleasant experiences of coming out of the warm womb into the cold world. Cold water Rebirthing has a way of Rolfing the energy body. [*Author. Rolfing is a kind of deep tissue massage developed by Ida Rolf and used to evoke emotions through physical contact.*] Rolfing is a way of stimulating and realizing pain that is stored in the human organism. The deepest levels of pain in the human organism can also be stimulated and realized through cold water Rebirthing. The basic technique here is to go in, one inch at a time, and integrate the sensations before going in the next inch. It could take half an hour to one hour to get into the water. The water can be any temperature as long as it is water and not ice so that you can't get into it.[26]

Apart from individual sessions, Rebirthing is also done in groups — either in pairs or as a group with one or more assistants. The group setting creates a certain dynamic that often facilitates the individual sessions, in particular by triggering psychophysical blocks. A person with strong blocks can be affected by emotional reactions that resemble their own from other group members. If several people have similar emotional reactions the effect is usually magnified.

Life energy

Since Rebirthing was developed mainly by people with no previous experience of psychotherapy, they found it difficult to find explanations for the strong experiences that the breath triggered. Besides, modern psychology does not offer many explanations for this kind of experience. As a consequence much of the theoretical framework is taken from the eastern cultures, in particular from India. The leading Swedish breathwork expert Bo Wahlström offers this explanation:

In the West there is a long tradition of health care within medical and psychiatric treatment. But when it comes to working with pure life energy there is a huge gap. It is like a missing part of a jigsaw puzzle. People are given a new opportunity when they learn to work directly with their life energy. In today's world many are so depressed that they lack energy to even start looking at their problems. They need more life energy in order to deal with their situation and to get inspired to initiate a change. They also need more energy in their bodies to be able to feel and experience themselves. You could say that the breath is our most unused natural resource that also contains the greatest potential for positive change.[27]

The energy cycle

According to Leonard Orr, Rebirthing is to breathe 'energy as well as air.' In order for a breathing session to have an effect the breathing pattern needs to become so open and relaxed that a person breathes both life energy and air. In the East this is called 'the inner breathing.' When a sufficient level of inner breathing is reached, the life energy sweeps through the body and cleans out 'stagnated and blocked energy.'

In Rebirthing the inner breathing is called 'energy cycle.' It is this cycle that is the potent part of the breathing and that determines the length of the session. Just as you can distinguish if a person is asleep by listening to the breathing pattern, the difference in the breathing during the energy cycle is clearly noticeable, even for the inexperienced. It becomes much more rhythmical and intense and is completely automatic and effortless. It often increases in intensity, reaches a climax and decreases gradually before it returns to a normal, calm breathing pattern. This is a totally spontaneous process that does not need any guidance. 'It was as if somebody took over and breathed for me,' is a common observation. It is not just the breathing that changes during the energy cycle. It usually leads to a 'bubbling' sensation throughout the body as if it had been 'carbonated.' It is usually a pleasant sensation that can start in one part of the body and spread throughout. Sometimes it is followed by sensations of sounds or lights or just a general feeling of wellbeing. It is often described as calmness and total harmony. The experiences are similar to those described in kundalini. When the energy cycle is completed the body releases energy. When the tensions are dissolved they can no longer block the body's inner energy. This turns instead to an additional energy injection that makes most people feel unusually vitalized and energetic after the session. Sondra Ray describes it as follows:

> The energy release gives you a new body. You feel connected to your body in a wonderful way — sensually — abundant physical energy and a sense of safety and serenity spreads over you.[28]

Leonard Orr offers the following explanation:

> A session is a complete energy cycle. The time the session takes is determined by the energy itself. The person goes inside himself. Energy moves in the body as well as in the mind. There is a dissolving of negative energy concentrations, which has an emotional basis as well as a physiological basis.
>
> The physical sensations that people experience can vary widely, as well as the mental and spiritual experiences. In the beginning of the practice the energy cycles are more physical. But it is hard to even make that generalisation because a person's internal experiences can be very different from the external appearance. But observing it objectively from the outside, there is more physiological action in the first five sessions or so, although internally it may just be the opposite. A person's physiological sensations might spark emotional fears and experiences inside, that preoccupy the person's rational

mind so that they hardly even observe the physiological phenomena that they are going through.[29]

*Recession (going back in the mind to a place beyond distinc-
tions and differentiations) can be frightening — it means losing ego identity. It is a state described in Buddhist literature
as no mind and no distinctions, a recession from multiplicity
to simplicity. If, in this way, you can get back to the mind
level where the confusions from a very early ontogenetic stage
arouse (and continue to arise in the mind), it is a lot less
messy than regressing in time.*

R.D. Laing

The Rebirthing breathing

A Rebirthing session comprises three principal breathing
patterns:

—*Deep and slow breathing* initiates the session and helps
  make the transition from everyday life. It also helps to
  increase relaxation before the more powerful breathing
  patterns start to trigger inner experiences. The session
  usually finishes with this same calm and slow breathing
  pattern, once the energy cycle has subsided. This helps
  the body to integrate the experiences.
—*Short and fast breathing* helps to trigger the energy cycle
  and to cope with strong emotions and body reactions.
—*Intensive and deep breathing* is used mainly in situations
  where memories make the body react so strongly that
  concentration is lost. This can be experienced as a sleep-
  like state. (In particular, experiences from the earliest part
  of childhood may trigger this reaction since sleep often is
  the only way the young baby can avoid traumas which are
  too painful.)

The ideal breathing pattern throughout the session is totally
relaxed and connected breathing. The breathing is spontaneous and completely effortless. Each breath is deep and
uses all of the breathing apparatus. The exhale follows

directly after the inhale without any pause. The exhale is totally relaxed. This breathing pattern follows when the body has adjusted and when sufficient tension has been released around the breathing apparatus to make the breathing completely unrestricted. It is often accompanied by a bubbling sensation throughout the body. The sensation is similar to the experience when the circulation returns to a part of the body that has been restricted, although more pleasant.

Cramp

If the emotional reactions during the session are painful or unpleasant, the body's natural reaction is to limit the breathing in order to regain control. If this is not noticed and the breathing pattern corrected, it may lead to cramp and a painful rigidity throughout the body that may dissolve spontaneously and quickly when the breathing is sufficiently relaxed.

Cramp is most common during the first Rebirthing sessions. This is because it may be difficult not to be overwhelmed by the emotions that the breathing may release. For most people it is a novel experience to let go of the control of the breathing and the emotions. Before a person feels safe in this situation the body will react by restricting the breath to block the release. But as the attempts to control the breath diminish the cramp tends to disappear.

When the most traumatic memories have been processed and integrated, the session often changes to be more calm and less eventful. The strongest experiences are often bodily sensations. The session often gives a sense of increased calm and peacefulness or energetic and positively 'charged.' Some sessions trigger everyday problems and bring increased insights, help solve problems or make important decisions, or raise creativity in general. The sessions become a way of 'charging' the body or mind to perform better than normal. Other common features (that we will examine in more detail later), are transpersonal experiences and altered states of consciousness.

Frank Lake's Rebirthing

There is another form of therapy that is also known as Rebirthing which, despite its name, has nothing in common with Leonard Orr's breathing technique. It was developed during the 1970s by the British psychologist Frank Lake who identified the importance of a therapeutic breathing pattern by way of drug therapy. This discovery made him abandon drugs for the Reichian breathing technique, which he saw as a safer method. Since many experiences which emerged were focused around birth, Lake and his assistants actively worked to re-create the events surrounding the birth, using pillows and mattresses which they pressed against the client, encouraging them to 'fight their way out.' Lake also organized visits to caves, and other confined spaces, so that participants could re-experience life in the womb. (It was a technique similar to this that led to a tragic death and consequent banning of all Rebirthing techniques in one American state some years ago.)

Some of our richest and most precious moments are held in our body memory; a smell, a touch, a look that stirs a longing, evokes a reawakening, bringing us back to something essential … The sense of a relationship or of a whole time period in our lives can be encapsulated in an image or a sensation. Yet, too the experience of painful and traumatic memories is deeply held in the body; connection with embodied experience gives a direct access to the unconscious, opening us to the immediacy of our subjective world.

Tree Staunton

The consequences of the birth process

It is not just our experiences during the period immediately after birth that are of extreme importance for our personal development. Our experiences preceding and during birth are also crucial. Fortunately, for most people birth is the most traumatic experience that they have to endure during their life. How good or bad the experience of our own birth is, may influence a person for the rest of their life. Until recently memories from birth were only accessible to us indirectly, via their influence on the unconscious mind later in life. What makes breathwork such a powerful psychotherapeutic tool is that it can put us in touch with experiences from our birth or even earlier.

Scientific evidence that we can remember what happened to us during this period of our lives, is quite new. It is only over the last thirty years that the development of new scientific equipment used in the study of foetus development combined with experiential evidence from breathing techniques has made this knowledge accessible. Earlier the newborn infant was considered to be insensitive to pain because its nervous system was not believed to be developed enough to experience it. As a consequence pain relief was considered unnecessary for infants under a certain age. Now we know that this has led to lifelong psychological scarring.

One reason why memories from so early in life were considered impossible to remember was the belief that the foetus could not have meaningful experiences, form memories or learn before its neocortex had been fully formed. It is now believed that the foetus has well-developed brain functions from the twentieth week of pregnancy. The foetus's brainwaves have been measured and found to react to visual stimuli, touch and sound from the seventh month. (Which confirms what all parents-to-be know instinctually — that it is possible to communicate with the unborn baby.)

The foetus's development

This new knowledge of prenatal development presents a very different picture of the foetus: it can now be regarded as a very able little individual, fully focused on preparing itself for life. It is trying out its muscles and lungs and it is listening and learning as best it can. When the nine months are up it is fully prepared and ready to meet the world.

These are some of the stages during this nine-month period:

—*At three weeks,* the brain starts to form with the appearance of a divide between the spinal cord and brain. This formation continues till the twelfth week: the upper part of the spinal cord develops into the brain stem and from this the middle and frontal parts of the brain are formed, with their characteristically 'wrinkled' surface which enables them to accommodate the maximum number of brain cells.

—*At six weeks,* when many women still are not sure they are pregnant, the embryo is around 2 cm long.

—*At seven weeks,* the face with eyes, nose, lips and tongue can be distinguished. The foetus produces beta-endorphins, which provide it with a sense of wellbeing.

—*At eight weeks* the hands and fingers start to form and the muscles start to move.

—*At ten weeks,* the body's basic structure is completed.

—*After three months,* the skeleton begins to take form and the foetus starts sucking its thumb. The breathing organs are being prepared to make the movements of the first breaths.

—*At four months,* the hypothalamus, which controls the body's inner chemistry, is functioning. The mouth is well developed and the foetus starts breathing amniotic fluids, which prepares the lungs for their continuous, life-long task. Throughout the remainder of pregnancy and during the first eight years of extra-uterine life the pleura that store air in the lungs continue to develop and grow. Consequently, it is especially important that small children have access to fresh air. Studies have shown that the foetus's breathing rhythm is disturbed by nicotine, caffeine, alcohol and other drugs. This can lead to inadequate breathing and/or reduced health throughout life.

—*At six months,* foetuses have been observed crying.

—*During the final three months* of pregnancy the foetus has more distinct periods of sleeping and waking and the brain shows a steady increase in activity and there is greater cooperation between its left and right sides.

A negative effect of this intense activity is that it makes the foetus extremely sensitive to its environment — that is to say, its mother. If the mother is exposed to stress, or exposes the foetus to stress because of her lifestyle, this may cause lifelong dysfunctions in the child, both of a physical nature and in the form of maladaptive behaviour. Studies have shown that animals in stressful and disturbed environments give birth to offspring with enlarged hindbrain. This makes the offspring more prone to aggressive behaviour. There is nothing to indicate that the same does not apply to human beings. Children who generally react via their survival instincts, rather than balancing these with rational thought processes, tend to be more aggressive and have less tolerance.[30]

Brain researchers have used great creativity in designing new methods of assessing the capabilities of unborn and newborn babies. One such method is the use of hypnosis to retrieve memories from this early phase of life. Even if many of these memories are fragmentary, it is often possible to verify that they are true and accurate memories. It has also been established that the child's experience of the birth may differ enormously from that of the adults present at the time of the birth. Even if the birth experiences are generally inexplicable to the baby (given that babies lack language and general knowledge of the world), people who have been able to remember their own birth do tend to interpret the memories correctly, in the sense that they have been able to give an 'adult' account of what happened. For instance, they will describe how somebody extracted the baby and held it by the legs, rather than simply recounting the fragmented experiences that must have been what the newborn baby was registering at the time.[31]

Modern medical technology has also made it possible to manipulate developments during pregnancy. The positive side is that this enables, for example, deformations to be prevented or remedied before birth, thus avoiding many complications and difficulties in later life. It has also meant that many infertile couples can have children. At the same time it also has a dark side, which is still not fully understood. For example, to surgically enter the womb and 'kill' surplus eggs (which is routine in IVF procedures) is beyond doubt a major trauma for the foetus. The consequences of this are not yet fully clear but some scientists claim that it may lead to serious and lifelong disturbance.

> *The systematic damage caused to children by insensitive treatment during birth in modern hospitals is much more dangerous than for instance smoking. The many relatively new problems — both physical, mental and social — which we see in today's children and teenagers may well be the effects of increased mechanization during birth.*
>
> Chilton Pearce

The effect of the birth

Even if birth can be a traumatic experience, it is important to remember that nature has prepared us to cope with the birth situation and, in fact, the whole birth sequence is an important part in the foetus's preparation for life. Both mother and child are clearly equipped with effective, hormone-induced programming to deal with the whole event. Even the pain has a role to play and the experience of pain triggers hormone release, mainly of endorphins that enable both mother and child to effectively cope with the pain.

What really creates trauma during birth is the interference of other people. Part of the natural programming of the mother is the impulse to isolate herself from others in order to give birth with as little outer disturbance as possible. This is how our ancestors gave birth for millions of years — and it was still generally the case up until about a hundred years ago. Today's hospitals, however, are about as far away from this kind of solitude as it is possible to get.

Despite the revelations of modern science, many hospitals continue to work as if newborn babies are completely insensitive and unable to experience pain. The maternity wards are designed to fit the needs of the hospital staff, with strong lighting, loud noises, an abundance of technical equipment and a generally sterile environment.

According to Michel Odent birth is one of the areas in which medical research is very poorly reflected in hospital routines.[32] An increasing number of studies show that unborn and newborn babies do not do well with the technical equipment and stressful environments of modern hospitals. One such example is ultrasound scanning, which is routine in many countries.

Disturbing the mother

It takes very little to disturb the birth process — strong lights and loud noise is enough. Even conversations between hospital staff during the birth can affect the child via the mother's reaction. There are many case studies in which adults, who have re-experienced their own birth, report how they were influenced by such comments during the birth. Chamberlain gives examples such as 'Wow, this looks like a sickly one!,' 'She's not important; take care of the mother!' or 'Look at her! We're lucky she was born at all, with all of these things wrong!'[33] These words, that the staff probably forgot having said within a few hours, can lead to lifelong psychological suffering for the infant involved.

Another very common source of disturbance is talking to the mother. During labour, it is the oldest parts of the brain that are active and in control of events. The brain's whole activity is concentrated in these most primitive parts. Talking to the mother forces her to divert some of her brain activity away to the neo-cortex, which deals with language. This disturbs the birth process — and it activates the part of the brain which is capable of worrying about the situation. The mother is also disturbed by strong lighting. If she feels observed it will also stimulate the neo-cortex. The same applies to all other disturbances because they lead to secretions of adrenaline — which again stimulate the neo-cortex.

If, on the other hand, the mother is undisturbed, and the younger parts of the brain remain inactivated, then hormone

The angry cat

This is a breathing exercise that works well during labour when the contractions are getting more intense. It helps to bring the breathing down into the abdomen which leads to increased oxygen intake as well as relaxation. It is usually done on hands and knees (hence the name), but it can be done in any position. If you feel secure enough, close your eyes (if not don't). Bring the teeth together without tensing the jaws. Separate the lips so that the teeth are visible. Breathe in and, on the exhale, let the air pass out between the teeth with a hissing noise hssssssss ... — just like an angry cat. Repeat this as many times as you feel comfortable with. Finish the exercise with a period of quiet and peaceful breathing.

releases will bring her into a very special state of mind. She will withdraw from the world and disappear into her own reality. In this world she is not her ordinary self. She becomes almost half animal, half human and can howl like an animal or move in ways which she normally would never dream of doing. It is therefore very desirable to ensure that the mother is completely undisturbed and in the safest possible environment. This is the best way to support the mother and make the birth process as easy as possible.

In order to help the child to exit the womb, there is an increase in the mother's adrenaline and nor-adrenaline level (fight-flight hormones). This reduces immediately after birth when the mother gets her first (in particular skin-to-skin) contact with the newborn baby, which triggers a release of the 'happiness' hormone oxytocin. It is still important that the environment is warm and free from loud noises and bright lights, since these would disturb this process. If the child does not get the time it needs in contact with the mother in a safe and calm environment the adrenaline level will not decrease according to schedule, which can lead to psychological shock. This, in turn, can prevent important brain functions from developing properly and lead to emotional and psychological disability that may persist for the rest of the baby's life. Such early disturbances may for instance diminish our ability to experience love.

A common practice in most modern hospitals during labour is to insert an electrode into the unborn baby's head to better monitor the baby's reactions. Research clearly indicates that this procedure causes so much disturbance that it certainly does more harm than good. In fact, it often causes emergency Caesarean deliveries. Other disturbing procedures are too early cutting of the umbilical cord, too early washing, weighing and measuring of the baby, or putting lapis into its eyes. There's no scientific evidence to confirm that any of this is necessary. On the contrary, cutting the umbilical cord too soon can lead to a panic reaction in the baby, forcing it to suddenly start breathing in order to avoid suffocation. Consequently, the baby is not given enough time, to calmly and gently, start using its lungs and to let them gradually expand and contract in their own time.

If the placenta is removed too early — before the umbilical cord has stopped pulsating — it can result in the baby losing half of its total blood volume. If the child is held above the placenta before the cord has been cut, the blood will flow back into the placenta. This may lead to an increased risk of respiratory problems. The placenta blood is very rich in iron and has many desirable qualities. Consequently, it is common practice in many hospitals today to store placenta blood for use in other treatment areas.

In a new method called 'Lotus Birth,' the placenta is left attached to the baby until it falls off by itself. To avoid infections, the placenta is washed and placed in a special container, kept next to the child. This has an overall positive effect on the child since it avoids 'placenta trauma.'[34]

Historical explanation

So despite the evidence from scientists, hospital staffs continue to justify routines that clearly disturb the birth process.

Why should this be? To find an answer we need to look back into our history. We can note that almost all cultures on our planet treat birth in similar dysfunctional ways — overriding our natural behaviour. The only exceptions are peoples still living as nomads and hunter-gatherers. In all other cultures the natural birth process is disturbed one way or another. A key example is often efforts to ensure that the newborn baby does not drink the first milk from the mother. Completely incorrectly, this is regarded as unhealthy whereas in fact it is extremely beneficial for the baby since it contains massive quantities of substances vital for the child's immune system.

But even if stress of this sort is bad for the mother and child, it may be good for society as a whole. It is good to be aggressive if you want to control the environment. And when humans converted from hunting (living in harmony with nature) to farming (controlling nature) they needed to control their environment. To disturb a child's entry into society also makes it easier to adapt the child to particular social patterns. So our keenness to disturb the birth process is deeply rooted. This is why hospitals continue to find medical 'excuses' for their traditional birth routines despite the growing evidence of the harm they do.[35]

Birth — a job for women

Another aspect of the modern hospital's deeply rooted tendency to disturb the birth process, is neglect of gender regarding those assisting: they make no distinction between male and female staff. However (without wishing to violate political correctness), we can state with a high degree of certainty that birth is a job for women. It is only during the last one hundred years or so that men entered into this female domain. In earlier epochs and in non-western cultures, men were banned from the birth process. It was always women who assisted. Contemporary science is indicating that this is built into our genetic heritage. Our natural behaviour requires that men keep their distance. Their role is to ensure that the mother is protected from any dangers in her environment. An explanation for this is the vital role of female sex hormones in the birth process. If men get too close they can interfere with and/or disturb the release of these hormones, especially through the presence of men with whom the mother is unfamiliar.

Statistics confirm that a large number of children are born when the father-to-be leaves the room. Some scientists also argue that if the baby's first contact is with the father, rather than the mother, this may activate 'motherly' behaviour in the father. So, instead of getting a mother and a father, the child may end up with two 'mothers' fighting to own the same role. This can also have negative effects on the couples' sex life due to confusion over their sex-roles.[36]

Nothing happens to anybody which they are not fitted by nature to bear.

Marcus Aurelius

Breathing and birth

In the beginning of the 1950s new methods of facilitating the birth process which utilized breathing techniques were developed. The new ideas came mainly from Russia and were based on the theories of Ivan Petrovich Pavlov (more famous for his dog-training experiments). These ideas were introduced to Europe and the USA by Ferdinand Lamaze under the name *Childbirth Without Pain*. At the same time the English obstetrician Grantley Dick-Read developed a natural birth method that he called *Childbirth Without Fear*. Later the American obstetrician, Robert A. Bradley, developed the Bradley-method, which was influenced by these European schools. Bradley wanted the father to be present during the birth. He also encouraged mothers, via special exercises, to express and rid themselves of negative emotions before the birth rather than during it.

These new methods taught pregnant women to relax and to concentrate on breathing correctly. The positive effects included an increased oxygen supply, which improves muscle response during contractions, making the birth process easier. The breathing exercises also helped the mother to maintain a better mental balance. These days it is common practice to teach prophylactic breathing techniques as part of pregnancy classes, and these are, in fact, a legacy from these early developments.

Unfortunately many parents-to-be reacted negatively to the new natural birth methods: they found them stressful in that pressure was put on the mother to be 'brave' and give birth without pain relief. This led to a trend in the opposite direction — namely, an effort to make the birth process more and more 'mechanical.' Part of this has been an attempt to move the responsibility for the process away from the mother, as much as possible, and place it almost entirely in the hands of the hospital staff (since a sedated mother can't do much to assist). In particular in the USA this has led to an absurdly high number of Caesarean sections — which, after all, is the ultimate way of controlling the birth process. Many obstetricians are simply afraid of getting sued for huge amounts by dissatisfied parents.

An alarming development which has emerged in conjunction with the 'mechanization' of birth, is the increase in infant mortality in the USA. Even though there are no clear links between the two, the fact remains that the statistics in the USA are worse than those of comparable industrial countries and there is no well-established explanation.

Feelings in themselves do not necessarily lead to wisdom
But the process of opening fully to them can.

John Welwood

Holotropic Breathwork

The other major modern breathing technique developed and registered in the West is Holotropic Breathwork. As we saw above, Holotropic Breathwork was developed in the USA by the Czech psychiatrist Stanislav Grof and his wife Christina.

During the 1960s Grof undertook pioneering work with clinical LSD-therapy. This work started at the Psychiatric Research Institute in Prague and continued in USA where he was Head of Psychiatric Research at the Maryland Psychiatric Research Center and Assistant Professor of Psychiatry at John Hopkins University in Baltimore.

After observing a great number of patients in their reactions to drug-induced experiences, Grof came to appreciate the role of the breathing during such experiences. When the use of drugs in clinical studies became restricted due to new legislation, and research into the effects of hallucinogenic drugs became more difficult to conduct, Grof started to encourage his patients to follow the breathing patterns he had observed in the LSD-therapy, as a stand-alone exercise. In 1973 Grof was invited to the Esalen Insitute in Big Sur, California, where he lived and worked as a Scholar-in-Residence until 1987. During this time, he and his wife Christina developed the technique to be known as Holotropic Breathwork. Grof soon discovered that this new technique resulted in similar deep inner experiences, but with the bonus that they suffered none of the dramatic physical side effects that can accompany drug-induced therapy.

In order to define and describe the experiences he recorded, Grof coined the word 'holotropic' experiences. The word *holotropic* derives from the Greek words *holos* (whole) and *tropein* (to move forward or towards something), thus moving towards the whole. Grof distinguishes this from the *hylotropic* cosmic process that moves towards the material world.

Here we look at some physical aspects of the Holotropic Breathwork experience, and in the next section we examine in more detail the 'transpersonal' nature of certain experiences.

Although Holotropic Breathwork has many things in common with Rebirthing (and is therefore often assumed — incorrectly — to be the same as Rebirthing) they are two completely different techniques. In short, Rebirthing has more focus on the breathing pattern than Holotropic Breathwork, where an understanding of how the mind works (as provided by Grof's cartography of the psyche) and a nurturing therapeutic setting are regarded as more important factors to evoke the natural healing potential. In Holotropic Breathwork too, a deeper and more effective breathing is encouraged. The breathing pattern resembles Rebirthing, but there is no direct intention to establish a specific breathing pattern.

The breathers are encouraged to listen to their body's signals, and to act them out in sounds and movement. The aim is to bring out emotions that for some reason have not been fully experienced, in order to reach a state of completion and integration. When an emotion has been fully experienced, it ceases having an unconscious influence and becomes a part of the conscious memory.

Holotropic Breathwork can be done individually or in pairs in a group setting. The session takes place with the individual lying on their back (as in Rebirthing). Music is used to help stimulate and amplify the emotional reactions. Ideally it should be unknown and wordless, to avoid stimulation of the neocortex rather than the emotional centres in the brain. It is played loudly so it can effectively penetrate and affect both body and mind.

The role of the therapist is to be a general support and to create a safe space during the session. Integration of the non-ordinary into the ordinary is important to Holotropic Breathwork and it incorporates art, bodywork, and group sharing into the after-breathing part of the work.

The experiences in Holotropic Breathwork are very similar to those in Rebirthing. They range from present-time experiences back to birth and the time as a foetus (some even claim to have experiences from previous lives). Grof has categorized the experiences into a Cartography of the Psyche — in Biographical, Perinatal and Transpersonal. He has also identified a COEX system (a system of condensed experiences) that he defines as:

A dynamic constellation of memories (and associated fantasy material) from different periods of the individual's life, with the common denominator of a strong emotional charge of the same quality, intense physical sensation of the same kind, or the fact that they share some other important elements.[37]

The COEX system shows how some experiences in all three of these categories can happen concurrently in a session because of their link through emotion or sensation. The different experiences may lead back to a number of core experiences — often from the time in the womb, around birth, early infancy or childhood — that are re-experienced in a number of different versions during repeated breathing sessions.

The reason why they recur is that first life impressions influence how we perceive similar incidents later in life. The way we remember guides us to bring together similar experiences to form a cluster of memories. An experience is not fully integrated until the original incident has been re-experienced.

With the perfect synchronization of interior and exterior rhythms, one can follow the path of least resistance and float freely in the ocean of the phenomenal world without getting drowned. To be precise, the human body is the most perfect instrument for the expression of consciousness.

Harish Johari

Transpersonal experiences

One consequence of the introduction of techniques such as Holotropic Breathwork and Rebirthing is that more and more people in the West are starting to have experiences which go far beyond the individual's previous model of reality — 'transpersonal experiences.' The word 'transpersonal' refers to the fact that these experiences take a person beyond the personal, and involve a feeling of having reached a reality beyond everyday life. In particular, in situations where a person is brought close to the very deepest meaning of existence, this may lead to a change of awareness. Time and space cease to exist, and the individual experiences a feeling of being at one with the universe.

Experiences of this type do not fit in with conventional psychology, in that there is no theoretical framework to support them. This has brought psychology to a level that requires new theoretical support. Not everyone in conventional psychology has been willing to take this step, and this has lead to a split between advocates of the varying views.

In the East, where no difference is understood between psychology and spirituality, such experiences are well known and documented. They occur when a person has cleared enough internal energy blocks, so that the inner life energy (kundalini) starts to move through the body.

In the East, the western role of psychotherapist is held by a spiritual master who is obliged to teach only what he has experienced, unlike the western psychotherapist who may not have undergone transpersonal experiences. Another difference is that the eastern approach is to actively teach the student to aim for a higher consciousness, while the western psychotherapist will focus on the psychological problems that may follow a transpersonal experience; problems which are caused mainly by ignorance or misunderstanding.

An important aspect of the eastern approach is therefore to prepare the student carefully for this type of spiritual experience, in order to minimize the risk of psychological problems. One way of doing this is to wait for the appropriate moment to initiate the experience, when the student is ready for what may come, both mentally and physically.

In the West, ignorance is still widespread despite the fact that there have always been people who have undergone spontaneous transpersonal experiences. In earlier times, these were given a religious connotation, which removed the need to try to understand them from a scientific point of view. (If you can't measure it, it is not science, and therefore it doesn't exist, was a common view.) Even today, there remains a great reluctance among scientists to acknowledge and accept emotions, a spiritual life and even consciousness — the existence of which some scientists deny, as they have not been able to locate it in the brain. They refer all speculations in this area to philosophy, religion or even to general confusion.

At the same time however there is a growing interest in perception, and brain functions aimed at exploring the human consciousness. At the forefront of this research are scientists who question the location of consciousness, and argue that it may not be in the human body at all — that the human brain is a receiver of consciousness rather than a creator of it. So while one end of the continuum argues that consciousness, at best, is a by-product of the brain's activities, the other end speculates as to whether the brain is really only the recipient of a higher consciousness (a kind of radio, tuned into information from the creator of our universe, or what Jung would describe as our collective unconscious).

> *The most beautiful experience we can have is the*
> * mysterious ...*
> *He to whom this emotion is a stranger, who can no longer*
> * pause to wonder*
> *and stand rapt in awe, is as good as dead.*
>
> Albert Einstein

The nature of mystical experience

Before the introduction of the term 'transpersonal experiences,' these events were commonly described as mystical experiences. Some people claimed to have several mystical experiences throughout their lives; whereas others never came close to an experience of this kind.

There are a number of attributes common in experiences

of this kind. They give a strong sense of reality and lead the person to believe that the experience is absolutely real and that it has a deeper meaning. There is a sense of togetherness.

It gives a feeling of being at one with other beings, with nature or with the whole universe. The experience is indescribable — literally as if there are no words to adequately convey what has happened. There is a sense of going beyond time and space. There is also a sense of a higher meaning — a spiritual meaning, or a strong feeling of happiness and peace. Yet there is a sense of something paradoxical taking place — that what has happened is impossible but still true. Or there is a sense of going through a positive change but that the experience is not a permanent state.

Transpersonal or mystical experiences occur spontaneously mainly in three particular circumstances in life. The first is around the creation of new life, during conception or the most intimate moments of the sexual act. As well as transpersonal experiences, close physical contact may also lead to physical or mental synchronization. One such example is breast-feeding. Another is the sexual act where the intense and close contact between two people may lead to a merging of emotions and thoughts. A similar closeness may also be experienced during guided breathworking sessions and psychotherapy. The emotional and physical openness in this kind of situation can make the boundaries between client and therapist so weak that the exchange of thoughts and emotions becomes more intense than normal.

Music, visual impression from art and beautiful landscapes, meditation or simply a quiet moment in the sofa with the cat on your lap, may also increase the body's production of endorphins. Some sweets that we like to eat have a similar effect and can also relieve pain. The body's own healing chemical substances (brain peptides) are 25,000 times more effective than ordinary pain killers. In other words it is scientifically proven that it works to eat sweets to compensate for physical and mental pain. One physiological explanation is that the experiences are a by-product of the body's ability to produce natural opiate mainly through excretion of endorphins that give a feeling of wellbeing.

The second situation that may trigger transpersonal experiences is around birth — when we witness how a new being starts the journey through life. In particular oxytocin (one of the hormones that control contractions of the womb and initiates breast-feeding) acts as a natural opiate and causes changes in awareness at the same time as it helps the body to handle pain.

The third situation is almost the opposite of the other two. It concerns situations when our life is in danger — and contact with death, either our own or when somebody close to us dies. Of course, both birth and death are in the 'no-man's land' between our everyday reality and the unknown worlds that all of us have to visit at some point. To suddenly come face to face with death can have the same effect on both young and old. As soon as our brain is developed enough to fully understand the meaning of dying, this kind of situation may lead to a spontaneous and powerful change of our consciousness. Usually the experience will change a person for life.

> *... dying is peaceful and beautiful, life does not begin with birth nor end with death, what matters most in life is love and seeking knowledge is important — you take that with you.*
> (A teenager's description of a near-death experience).[38]

Near-death experiences

Another type of phenomenon that has recently been receiving more attention concerns those situations when a person for some reason stops breathing completely — the near-death experiences (NDE). With advances in modern medicine it is increasingly common that a person who 'dies' can be brought back to life.

Since the 1970s there has been systematic research into the experiences people have claimed when they have been clinically dead — that is, when breathing has stopped completely, the heart has stopped beating and there is no brain activity. Since it is routine during operations to monitor body activity, there is no doubt that these people have been clinically dead, yet despite this they wake up telling fantastic stories of experiences that will forever transform their lives — experiences from the time they have been clinically dead. However, not all people who claim to have had near-death experiences have been clinically dead; some have these experiences when unconscious but with heart, lungs and brain still functioning.

One of the big issues that near-death experiences raises is where human consciousness is located. Since it in some cases has been proven beyond any doubt that the brain has been completely inactive, the experiences indicate that human consciousness also exists outside the brain. Experiences recorded in breathwork sessions indicate the same. It is not uncommon for people to claim to re-experience their own conception, even previous lives. This kind of experience is inexplicable within today's western medicine.

Since near-death experiences were first widely written about in the 1970s, a great number of books have been published on the subject. The various accounts provide a number of common core elements. One such is the feeling of having a 'silver thread' that acts as a link between the physical body and the consciousness, which is seen to be floating freely outside the body. After the experience the consciousness is brought back into the body via this thread. Another common experience is that 'life passes by.' It is like a film played back inside the head, from which each frame, each detail of the person's life from the very beginning, passes by. The images often lead to insights and explanations that provide a sense of positive completion. For many it also offers a real sense of forgiving others.

> ... *there is a reason for everything that happens. Find your own purpose in life and appreciate things for what they are — not for what they can give you and remember you are not your body.*
> (Teenage boy describing a near-death experience).[39]

Lack of oxygen

Some argue that it is lack of oxygen that causes mystical experiences and near-death experiences. The parts of the brain that control emotions are particularly dependent, and react quickly when they are starved of oxygen. One effect of low oxygen is very strong emotions — also a common feature in near-death experiences. But one argument against this theory is that the part of the brain that controls memory is no less dependent on oxygen. If near-death experiences were caused by oxygen deprivation this should mean that it would be impossible to remember the experience — which is not the case in most cases.

It is also known that breathwork techniques such as Rebirthing and Holotropic Breathwork can lead to similar experiences. In particular towards the end of a session, the person may sometimes stop breathing, in some cases for several minutes. Colour may disappear from the face, and the body may appear completely lifeless. Breathing usually restarts spontaneously, and many are completely unaware that they stopped breathing. There is currently no explanation as to why this occurs.

Some eastern breathing exercises are designed to slow down the breathing and prolong the pause between inhale and exhale, but here the process is highly controlled and may take years of regular practice to achieve. The pause (between inhale and exhale) is gradually extended so that long periods are spent completely without breathing. This gives a sense of inner peace in a similar way to meditation (where the goal is to find the space between thoughts).

During the 1950s the American psychiatrist L.J. Meduna carried out experiments, giving his patients a mixture of oxygen and carbon dioxide as a form of psychiatric treatment. This caused a number of his patients to have dreamlike experiences that had many similarities with near-death experiences. The patients described fantastic emotions, strong colours and geometrical patterns. Many also experienced a higher cosmic connection, whereas a small group has such horrible experiences that they woke up terrified.

The experiences had no direct connection with their psychological condition and were similar for all patients. The result of the oxygen-carbon dioxide mixture was that it gave a surplus of carbon dioxide in the blood. This was assumed to be the cause of the experiences. But this has been questioned since then, in particular when compared with near-death experiences, which in many cases come from patients who have been monitored very carefully and have certainly not been allowed to build up excess carbon dioxide in their blood. In addition (in the case of the modern breathing techniques) intensive breathing usually results in an actual reduction in carbon dioxide levels.[40]

Together, near-death experiences and transpersonal experiences have brought about the beginning of a new outlook on illness and death that is much closer to the traditional view originated by shamans. According to this view, the final goal is not always to avoid death. Illness has its origin and purpose in the spiritual world, and the healing process can therefore be seen as a form of spiritual development. The purpose of life is to learn from the spiritual world and to see how one interacts with everything else, both in this world and the spiritual world. Most important is to look after the soul, since if the soul is lost a person risks losing everything that gives meaning to life. It is when a person has lost their personal power, that illness, evil spirits or other physical or mental damage may occur. According to the anthropologist and shaman Michael Harner, these old views are so strongly rooted in human consciousness that ordinary cultural beliefs and theories are more or less irrelevant.

I was frightened, man. I figured the pressure was on me. I was between time and space.
> Bob Beamon describing his fantastic long jump
> record at the Olympic Games in Mexico 1968

Extreme physical performance

There is a fourth situation that may trigger spontaneous mystical experiences, although this is limited to a much smaller population. This is in extreme physical performances (above all, in sports) when suddenly everything works exactly according to plan and a person is able to push their body to the extreme limits in order to reach a desired goal. One explanation is that the body increases its endorphin levels during hard physical exercise.

> *If the only tool you have is a hammer,*
> *you tend to see every problem as a nail.*
>
> Abraham Maslow

Abraham Maslow

One of the important influences in transpersonal psychology comes from Abraham Maslow. Perhaps his most famous contribution is his 'hierarchy of needs' (that has many similarities with the chakra system) where he divides human needs into different levels.

Our most basic needs are linked with our physical survival (food and sleep). They are followed by a need for safety (every person has a need to feel secure in their life situation). But we also have a need to feel close to others; that we are part of the society we live in; and that we have people we care for and who we know care for us. In order to fulfil higher needs we need first, at least to some extent, to fulfil the lower needs. The highest needs in Maslow's hierarchy will only be fulfilled when the lower needs are met. The highest level is self-actualization.

To Maslow self-actualization was a central concept that he saw as closely linked with *peak experiences*. Maslow compared peak experiences with the mystic's experience of discovering their inner truth and realizing their true self (which he regarded as the key element in all religions).

In this type of experience, the universe is often seen as an entity, not just intellectually but as a kind of experience or direct realization of reality. Experiences of this sort can often have a decisive influence on an individual's outlook on life. They may be the result of religious activity, but can also be triggered spontaneously by everyday situations, such as seeing a beautiful landscape, listening to music or experiencing love for another person.

For Maslow, self-actualization meant the realization of our true self and our deepest desires, within the day-to-day context of our lives. In order to achieve this, a person needs to learn to listen to their inner voice and be willing to follow it. He also stated that experiences of this kind were in no way signs of psychological disorder and did not need medical attention. On the contrary, they often appear in people with no previous record of psychological or emotional problems, and whom experts of psychology would regard as perfectly normal.

Stanislav Grof

Another major influence on transpersonal psychology is the founder of the Holotropic Breathwork, Stanislav Grof, whose techniques we have already examined in the previous section. Although his first contact with transpersonal experiences was through LSD-therapy, he subsequently found that Holotropic Breathwork led to the same kind of experiences as certain states of altered consciousness.

Another and perhaps more common term for transpersonal experiences is *non-ordinary state of consciousness*. According to Grof this term is too comprehensive for the experiences in Holotropic Breathwork. Instead he prefers to define the holotropic states as:

> … characterized by a specific transformation of consciousness associated with perceptual changes in all sensory areas, intense and often unusual emotions, and profound alterations in the thought processes. They are also usually accompanied by a variety of intense psychosomatic manifestations and unconventional forms of behaviour.[41]

Although holotropic (or transpersonal) experiences are certainly not rare, conventional psychiatry has little understanding of them and they are conventionally diagnosed as acute psychosis. But Grof argues against this position:

> Consciousness is changed qualitatively in a very profound and fundamental way, but unlike in the delirant conditions, it is not grossly impaired. In holotropic states, we experience intrusion of other dimensions of existence that can be very intense and even overwhelming. However, at the same time, we typically remain fully oriented and do not completely lose touch with everyday reality. We experience simultaneously two very different realities.[42]

In addition our sensory perception may change. Colours and forms are intensified and change appearance. Physical sensations, smell, taste and sound are experienced differently. Inner images are common, both personal and mythological. Visions and experiences are common (those which Carl Jung called archetypal and believed to originate in our collective unconscious). The emotions vary from ecstasy, to heavenly peace, to overwhelming rage, despair, fear and guilt and are usually much stronger than in everyday life. The experiences of fear have many similarities with the description of hell in many religions. The physical experiences can be strongly exaggerated, from an experience of wellbeing and health to the absolute opposite, with feelings of pain, nausea and suffocation. The thought process also changes and can lead to many new ideas and insights. These can range from psychological insights, to insights about the origin of the universe, and may widely extend the education and intelligence of the person experiencing them. It is common that people who have had transpersonal experiences start to notice synchronicities (finding that there is a deeper meaning behind apparently unrelated events). Without proper guidance, these may not always be experienced as something positive.

Grof also points out that a common mistake concerning archetypes is to see one specific symbol as the most significant, while an archetype in fact merely describes a set of characteristics, or an energy formation. For example, to perceive Jesus as a symbol for a higher being is common, in particular among Christians. But to assume that Jesus is the only symbol for a higher being is false. It does not matter if the symbol in the experience is Jesus, Buddha, Allah, a garden rose or any other image that illustrates the highest — the experience is a personal interpretation. The important part is what the specific symbols in an experience mean to each individual. This common mistake is one of the main causes of religious conflicts. In particular, when the symbol is connected with strong emotions and experiences, many are willing to fight for their conviction and this has been one of the main causes of war and conflicts since the beginning of human history. It is then extremely important to understand that an archetype can take many shapes and forms, and yet still have the same source.[43]

Grof also highlights another common mistake (in particular in New Age circles) — that of having too limited an interpretation of a transpersonal experience where the individual has the feeling of being 'creator of their own reality.' In a holotropic state of mind, a person may experience that they have chosen their own destiny, their parents and the environment where they have incarnated, quite literally. But even if this may be the ultimate reality of all phenomena in the universe, this is not to say that it is directly applicable to everyday life. To see oneself as the creator and ultimately responsible for everything that happens in daily life is entirely wrong, and to follow this argument through may lead to feelings of guilt that are very difficult to handle. If a person, perhaps a relative, falls ill or dies, this is not necessarily of their own doing.

Equally, to say that all that happens in the world is perfect (another common New Age perception), based on this view, may instead lead to endless cruelty and insensitivity. It is like saying that a person run over by a car has chosen this destiny for themselves. Even if this should be the ultimate truth, it should of course never prevent the individual from acting in a way that is inappropriate or less than morally acceptable in an everyday context.

How come that when we talk to God it is called prayer,
but when God talks to us it is called schizophrenia?

Lili Tomlin

Spontaneous transpersonal experience

When a person has a spontaneous transpersonal experience the first reaction is often fear. It feels as if something big and overwhelming is taking place, but it is difficult to say what and why this is happening. If the experience is strong, it may lead the person to seek medical help, where the most likely reaction is a referral to the psychiatric specialist. Since information is limited in this area, it is difficult to say how often this happens and if the prescribed treatment actually has an effect. According to Grof there are too many cases of incorrect treatment of people who seek help in the belief that they have incurred some sudden and permanent mental illness, rather than a momentary change of consciousness.

In order to increase awareness of this area both generally and within the psychiatric domain, Stanislav and Christina Grof started a worldwide network called *Spiritual Emergence,* aimed at helping therapists to understand and treat holotropic experiences and to assist the person through their acute crisis in a way that does not lead to psychological scarring. (At the time of writing this network is not active.)

Grof also argues that there is a need for a wider understanding of the human psyche. He suggests two areas in particular. The first concerns experiences before and during birth. The second concerns holotropic (or transpersonal) experiences that lead to an increased sense of identification with elements outside the own body and with other realities.

The emergency situations that Grof's network was designed to help with may have at their source a phenomenon known in the East as spontaneous awakening or kundalini. If a person is unprepared or without assistance, this process may lead to several psychological disorders. It is no coincidence that cultures with knowledge of the body's internal power see it as vital to move slowly and patiently, to give the body and mind the time it needs to prepare for the experience. This is the only way to protect against unwanted experiences that, once initiated, are difficult to control.

It is certainly not desirable to try to awaken the flow of kundalini before the body and mind are ready, since there is no guarantee that the experience will have a positive effect. Nevertheless, it is becoming more common for modern shamans to use the breath to awaken the inner forces as quickly as possible, and usually with a lack of respect for what may go wrong. The temptation is what is perceived as the end result — to gain inner power and superhuman abilities. This approach demonstrates a lack of insight and respect for what it takes to achieve such power. In the East this is regarded as a kind of 'spiritual materialism,' meaning that a person is trying to achieve results for which s/he is not mentally and spiritually ready. A similar situation in the western world is created by recreational drugs. These may lead to a spontaneous non-ordinary state of consciousness for which the taker may be completely unprepared. Where the effects are damagingly negative, such consequences may lead to extensive and long psychiatric treatment.

Spiritual bypassing

John Welwood describes a similar phenomenon that he calls *spiritual bypassing*.[44] He refers to people — in particular westerners pursuing a spiritual path — who adopt (mainly eastern) spiritual theories and exercises as a (probably unconscious) way of avoiding emotional and psychological problems. However, claims Welwood, in many cases these are problems that conventional western psychotherapy is better at handling than the eastern philosophies.

The lack of current western theories that incorporate transpersonal experiences has led to a new form of east-western psychotherapy that aims at broadening the western view and adapting it to integrate eastern wisdom. One of the best known forms for this is Buddhist psychotherapy. Buddhism is probably the eastern religion that has had the greatest impact on modern psychotherapy, maybe because it best caters for the western need for logic and intellectual explanations.

John Welwood, who is one of the leaders when it comes to merging eastern and western psychology, gives the following explanations:

> Eastern contemplative psychology, based on meditative practice, presents teachings about how to achieve direct knowledge of the essential nature of reality, which lies beyond the scope of the conventional conceptual mind. Western therapeutic psychology, based on clinical practice and conceptual analysis, allows us to trace specific causes and conditions influencing our behaviour, mind-states, and self-structure as a whole ... Indeed, beyond the differences of geography, race, and culture, East and West ultimately represent two different aspects of ourselves. In this sense, they are like the relationship between breathing out and breathing in. The eastern emphasis on letting go of fixation on form, individual characteristics, and history is like breathing out, while the western emphasis on coming into form, individuation, and personal creativity is like breathing in. And just as breathing in culminates in breathing out, so breathing out culminates in breathing in. Each side, without the other, represents only half of the equation.[45]

3. Healing and the Breath

When breath control is perfected, the body
    becomes light,
countenance becomes cheerful, eyes become bright,
digestive power increases, and it brings internal
    purification and joy.
                    Grahayamalatantra, Chapter 13

Before we can improve the way we breathe, it is essential to understand exactly how we breathe and what happens in the body when we breathe.

At the same time it is of course interesting to consider whether there is any scientific backing to the claim that breathing means more than simply introducing oxygen to the body. Is there any evidence that 'life energy' exists? Is there any scientific proof that breathing exercises have a positive effect on both body and mind? The fact that breathing exercises have been used to cure illness in places lacking modern western medical resources is one thing, but does that also mean that breathing exercises have a place in modern medicine?

To answer questions like these we need to take a closer look at the various aspects of the respiratory process, and what role breathing plays in modern medicine.

The respiratory system

Many parts of the body and many internal functions are involved when we breathe, and these are initiated and coordinated by the respiratory centre in the medulla oblongata, or hindbrain. Usually this operates as a reflex, drawing on information from sensory feedback mechanisms in the lungs and the muscles, and from the oxygen-carbon dioxide balance in the blood.

The signals are initiated according to the level of carbon dioxide, rather than amount of oxygen present, but they can also be triggered by emotions and controlled by the will.

One group of nerve cells in the hindbrain initiates inhalation, and another exhalation. Inhalation is an active process initiated by an impulse from the vagus nerves; exhalation is the reverse, a relaxation of the muscles involved, caused by inhibition of the impulse.

The air we breathe in is made up of approximately 20 per cent oxygen and .03 per cent carbon dioxide, with the balance comprising nitrogen, water vapour and other gases including carbon monoxide, methane, helium and air pollution. The air we breathe out comprises approximately 14 per cent oxygen, 5 per cent carbon dioxide, 6 per cent water vapour, 69 per cent nitrogen and other gases excreted by the body's metabolism.

Oxygen is the single most important substance for the body. In order for the body to function, all cells must regularly be supplied with oxygen which they can transform into energy. Carbon dioxide also plays an important role. The most important task undertaken by the breathing process is to supply the body with oxygen through inhalation, and to remove waste products through exhalation. The apparatus that makes this possible consists of the nasal and sinus passages, windpipe, bronchi and lungs.

When we breathe, we inhale through the nose, which is the natural pathway for air to enter the body. The nose is designed to filter and warm the air before it reaches the lungs. Inhaling through the mouth fails to give the same cleaning and temperature adjustment, and the difference can be significant especially if the surrounding air is polluted or very cold.

The shape of the nose is decided by the particular climate for which we are designed. In colder climates, a long nose will warm the air up more effectively before it reaches the lungs. In dry climates, a long nose acts as an air moisturiser as well as a particle filter. In warm and wet climates, a short broad nose with large nostrils is preferable, as the air needs less adjustment before it gets into the body: it is also easier to breathe if the airway is more open, and this saves energy which can be valuable in hot climates.

The nose is divided into two narrow cavities by a partition called the septum, made of bone and cartilage. The outer ends of the cavities, the nostrils, are lined with fine hairs that filter out dust and bacteria from the air we breathe. The septum is covered by a mucous membrane that moistens and warms up the air. (When too many particles accumulate on the membrane a sneezing spasm will be triggered to expel them.) The two cavities, called the nasal fossae, are very narrow, less than 6 mm wide. The cavity at the back of the nose is divided into long thin sections by three ridges of bone. The passage is lined with mucous membrane with a rich blood supply. The membrane secretes half a litre of mucus per day. The sinuses or cavities in the front of the skull are connected with the nose, and they form a triangle behind the eyebrows and the cheeks on either side of the nose.

Most of the time, the air does not pass equally through the two nasal passages; one side tends to be open wider than the other as blood flow shifts between the nostrils at around ninety minute intervals. This rhythm has to do with the brain function in the two halves of the brain.

After being inhaled through the nose, the air passes through the pharynx and down through the larynx and trachea. The pharynx is the cavity at the back of the mouth that links the nose with the mouth, and where the pharyngeal plexus oversees the coordination of swallowing and breathing. This activity is controlled from the lower brain stem. The main role of the larynx in the breathing process is to assist the vocal cord in using breath to produce sound.

The upper part of the trachea is at the front of the throat. It is about 10 cm long and 2.5 cm wide. From the

Alternative nostril breathing

The body's ability to heal itself can be improved by actively guiding the breath to either side of the nose. This gives increased inner balance. It can also ease headache.

Sit with the back as straight as possible and make sure nothing is restricting the breathing. Lift one hand and hold it in front of the nose so that the thumb rests lightly against one nostril. Close the fingers so that the index finger and ring finger rest lightly against the opposite nostril. Breathe out. Then put light pressure with the thumb so that air only passes through the opposite nostril, and breathe in. Lift the thumb and apply light pressure with the fingers against the other nostril. Breathe out through the opposite nostril. Breathe in through the same nostril, and change pressure again before you breathe out, then in again. Continue to breathe, through alternative nostrils, by blocking one nostril at a time for each exhale/inhale cycle, for around ten minutes. Complete the exercise and return to normal breathing.

By breathing through one nostril at the time the different halves of the brain are stimulated in turn. According to yoga teaching, the left part of the brain corresponds to energy from the sun and the right part to energy from the moon. The nostrils are also entrances for the body's pranic system that introduces and circulates prana throughout the body. The right nostril leads to *pingala* — the positive *nadi* that raises the body's energy. The left leads to *ida* — the negative *nadi* that calms the body.

trachea the air continues down into the chest cavity where the bronchi separate and lead into the right and left lungs. The trachea and bronchi are held open, like hollow tubes, by cartilaginous rings in their walls. Mucous membrane moistens the trachea and bronchi, and is covered with hair-like cilia, which function as traps for particles of dirt in the incoming air. The cilia move in an upward direction that sweeps any particles back up into the mouth. When too many particles are accumulated it triggers a cough reflex.

In the lungs the air-filled bronchi divide into ever-finer branches, called the secondary and tertiary bronchi, and to even smaller tubes called bronchioles. These, in turn, lead to clusters of air-filled sacs, called alveoli. The blood-filled pulmonary arteries form a secondary system of tubes, and they enter the lungs alongside the bronchi branches. The smaller tubes all contain blood vessels as they run alongside the bronchi, and they too divide again into capillaries — their equivalent of the alveoli.

There are around 750 million alveoli and capillaries in the lungs, and this is where the gas exchange with the blood actually takes place. The capillaries are so fine that blood cells can only pass through in single file, which means the cells are exposed to oxygen over their full surface area.

The oxygen is taken up by the haemoglobin in the blood. Haemoglobin gives the blood its red colour, and consists of a ferrous substance called *haem* and protein *(globin)*. Because oxygen is alkaline, and carbon dioxide acid, this initiates an exchange by a chemical reaction to neutralize the acid and the alkali. At the same time as the oxygen is absorbed by the blood, the red blood cells discharge carbon dioxide back into the alveoli, for onward delivery out of the body through exhalation.

From the alveoli the blood, now enriched with oxygen and nutrients from the food we eat, flows to the left chamber of the heart, which distributes it to all parts of the body. At each body cell a second exchange takes place, as nutrients from the blood are exchanged for waste products, in the form of carbon dioxide which is carried back to the lungs in a never-ending cycle.

The oxygenized blood from the heart vitalizes, nourishes and strengthens the body. On the way out from the heart the blood is bright red and vital, filled with life-giving qualities. On its return journey it is like a sewage ditch filled with waste products from the body.

Which nostril do you use?

If you want to test yourself, take a short break from reading and try to work out which side of the nose is more open. Notice how this feels and repeat the exercise at half-hour intervals until you notice a change to the other nostril.

According to yoga teaching, which nostril we breathe through is important, and there are exercises aimed at training people how to select which nostril, depending on the activity to be undertaken. Breathing more through the right nostril makes a person more active and aggressive, more alert and focused on the outside world. It also helps digestion, so it is good to open up the right nostril before a meal. To breathe mainly through the left nostril gives a more passive state of mind with an inner world focus. When you go to bed, a tip is to first rest on the left side in order to raise the body temperature. When the body is warm enough it is better to turn over to the right side to help the body to relax and fall asleep.

The lungs

The average lungs of an adult weigh between one and one-and-a-half kilograms. The different sides vary slightly in size, the right being the larger, as the heart takes up some of the space in the left side of the thorax.

Each lung is divided into lobes: the right lung into three, the left into two. Each lung can move freely in all directions except at the root, which principally comprises the tubes and arteries that connect it to the windpipe and heart.

The lungs are spongy and porous with a very elastic tissue

which, if flattened out, would cover around one hundred square metres. They are covered by a double layer of smooth membrane, like a strong bag. This is connected to the lungs at one side, and to the inside of the chest cavity at the other. Between the layers of membrane a fluid is excreted which makes it possible for the surfaces to glide against each other without friction. The fluid also holds the lungs open, by surface tension. (Like a drop of water can hold two sheets of glass together, so that they can only be separated by a sideways, sliding movement.) If the lungs are removed from the chest they would collapse like deflated balloons.

The lungs are pulled open when the chest is expanded. When we exhale, the rib muscles relax gradually, otherwise the lungs would spring back immediately. Even when we breathe out as much as we can, around one litre of air remains in the lungs to prevent them from collapsing. However, if through injury, air gets in between the lung and the membrane wall the surface tension breaks, and the lungs will collapse.

When we stand up, gravity forces more blood into the lower parts of the lungs than the upper, with a relatively greater gaseous flow in the upper part. Exactly how efficient the exchange is depends on the way we breathe. Shallow breathing (all too common in the adult population) results in a less efficient exchange. If, in addition, the surface of the lungs has been damaged by smoking or air pollution, the area where the exchange takes place is drastically reduced, and can lead to the condition known as emphysema. This illness develops slowly over time, and is indicated often through a general deterioration of the body's performance — for example, getting more out of breath than usual with physical exercise.

The Diaphragm

When we inhale the diaphragm contracts. The diaphragm is the large cupola-formed muscle that stretches over the ribcage and separates the chest cavity from the abdomen. The movement of the diaphragm is almost as automatic as the movement of the heart muscle, although the diaphragm can also be affected by the will.

When the diaphragm contracts the chest cavity expands, which expands the volume of the lungs. This creates a vacuum in the lungs and new air rushes in to fill the space. The lungs are filled from the bottom up (as when a bottle is filled). When we breathe out the diaphragm relaxes which decreases the space in the chest cavity and consequently in the lungs. This forces the air out of the lungs. Inhalation is the only active part. Exhalation is a completely passive relaxation of the muscles that contracted during inhalation.

The diaphragm is controlled by the autonomic nervous system that also controls how we react to stimuli from the world around us. The autonomic nervous system has a sympathetic and a parasympathetic function. In stressful situations the body's defence mechanisms are activated through the sympathetic system. Among other effects, it leads to a tightening of the muscles in the abdomen with a restrictive effect on the diaphragm. In other words, all forms of stress, fear and other negative emotions cause a disturbance in the respiratory process. The stress reaction also involves tensed muscles on the back, stomach and around the hips, which can cause an increase of the carbon dioxide level in the blood, which in turn has a negative effect on the respiratory process.

When we on the other hand breathe fully and openly, the movement of the diaphragm has a positive effect on the body. Since the diaphragm also has direct contact with the oesophagus, the blood circulation and certain nerves from the medulla, it massages, directly or indirectly, the stomach, liver, pancreas, intestines and kidneys. It also improves the movements of the intestine, the flow of the blood and the lymphatic system, and our ability to absorb nutrients.

Even the heart rate is affected by the way we breathe. If we breathe high up in the chest this requires more effort to achieve the same oxygen intake as abdominal breathing. More blood needs to be circulated through the lungs, which means that the heart has to work harder.

Training the diaphragm

Through Taoist breathing exercises it is possible to train the diaphragm to increase its movement by around four mm over a period of six to twelve months. This increases the volume of air in the lungs by more than one litre in a year or less. A normal breath consists of around 500 millilitres of air, whereas the total capacity of the lungs is around five litres. Each millimetre that the diaphragm expands is equivalent to an increased volume of air in the lungs of around 250 to 300 millilitres. The diaphragm is sometimes said to be a 'spiritual' muscle. According to the master Mantak Chia: 'Lifting the heart and fanning the fires of digestion and metabolism, the diaphragm muscle plays a largely unheralded role in maintaining our health, vitality, and wellbeing.'[46]

The brain

Some of the cells in the body can function for a short period without oxygen; the brain, however, cannot be deprived of oxygen without damage. The amount of oxygen delivered to the brain depends on a number of factors. It depends not only on how much oxygen is brought into the lungs, but also the oxygen level in the blood, and how quickly the oxygen is transported out to the body tissues. This, in turn, is related to the blood pressure. How well the cells absorb oxygen is also important. A low level of oxygen in the blood does not necessarily mean that the brain is receiving too little oxygen.

Not all parts of the brain are equally sensitive to a lack of oxygen; those parts that deal with emotions are particularly oxygen sensitive. A consequence of oxygen deprivation is that mystical experiences may be triggered, and it has been suggested that this can be one cause of near-death experiences (NDE). However, this is contradicted by the fact that the memory function is no less oxygen sensitive,

---

Tibetan breathing exercises

In Tibet breathing exercises known as *lung-gom* are used to heal the body and increase longevity. The exercises are based on the fact that, of around 20,000 breaths we take each day, around 500 have a specially vitalizing effect. By learning to control the breath the effect of these vitalizing breaths can be increased.

---

which means that a person experiencing a NDE should not be able to remember it, which is usually not the case.

The breathing rhythm

The breathing rhythm is the time it takes to breathe in and out. When we breathe fully and openly, the inhale is as long as the exhale. If breathing is restricted, the length of the inhale and exhale is usually not the same. When we breathe calmly, without physical activity or psychological reactions we breathe around 12–15 times per minute when we are awake, and between 6 and 8 times while we are asleep.

Men breathe somewhat slower than women, around 12–14 times per minute, while women breathe around 14–15 times. Newborn babies breathe about twice as fast as adults. Our breathing rhythm is not always directly linked with how much air we breathe in per minute. When we are resting we breathe in around half a litre of air which means 6.5 litres per minute or more than 8000 litres per 24 hours.

The True Man breathes with his heels,
the mass of men breathe with their throats.

Chuang Tzu

The air

Just like any machine, human beings need energy to function. The energy comes from a kind of slow combustion process called metabolism, which can be compared to an ordinary combustion engine where fuel and oxygen is mixed to extract energy. The fuel for the human combustion process comes mainly from carbohydrates and fats in the food we eat. In order to extract the right kind of energy, the combustion has to have the right conditions, and these are found in a part of the cell called the mitochondria. These contain special protein molecules, enzymes that transfer the energy from the food to the body's cells, which in turn carry out the chemical reactions that are necessary for the cells to function properly.

Since the amount of oxygen has a direct link with the body's energy conversion; the way we breathe has a direct link with how much energy the body gets. The various body functions are directly linked with the respiratory process and interact with the breathing on many levels. In particular, breathing is an important part in the continuing process that keeps the heart moving, supplies the body with oxygen, breaks down food to energy in order to keep the processes going and helps to eliminate waste products.

Another part of this process is to repair body parts and functions that have been damaged, to replace cells, and make the hair and nails grow. It is a continuous process that takes place entirely without our conscious involvement, just like breathing and the maintenance of the heartbeat. It means that the body knows exactly how to repair damage and keep the inner functions going in the best possible way. Everything is automatic, provided we do not interfere with the process.

This is important to remember, as when the body has been damaged or affected by illness, it will spontaneously react by trying to regain inner balance in the most effective way. The symptoms of ill health can in this way be indications of the body working to regain inner balance, and incorrect breathing can be one of those signs that the body is compensating for inner imbalance. This is important in the context of learning more about how improved breathing can lead to improved health. According to Robert Fried the question to ask is*:* 'What do I have to do to make it unnecessary for my body to have to make this particular adjustment that we call a disorder?'[47]

Preventing shortness of breath

To be out of breath is usually related to physical exercise or psychological stress. One way to prevent shortness of breath is to increase the exhale (since this means that we automatically have to inhale more). Open the mouth when you exhale and let the air flow out in a loud *haaaaaaaa.*

Waste elimination

The cells use a combination of oxygen and sugar as fuel, and this is converted into energy. The waste products in this process are mainly carbon dioxide and water. One of the most important ways for the body to eliminate waste products is through the breath. Only three per cent of all waste products are eliminated through the faeces, seven per cent through urine and 20 per cent through the skin; the remaining 70 per cent is eliminated through exhalation.

If a human being does not breathe enough fresh air, the blood cannot be completely cleaned. This means that waste products that should have been eliminated during oxygenation are brought back into the body so that, instead of enriching and rebuilding the body, the blood is conveying toxins around the system. This is like being poisoned by polluted air. Insufficient breathing also has a negative effect on the lymphatic system that is designed to trap and destroy viruses and bacteria before they cause damage to the body. Insufficient breathing also lowers the content of gastric fluids and enzymes with a negative effect on the metabolism. The passage through the intestine also slows down and leads to a build-up of waste deposits.

Constipation is more common in the industrial world than the third world. One reason is that we don't breathe deeply enough to dispose of enough waste products through the exhalation. Another reason is that we use deodorants that prevent the skin from breathing. The amount of processed food we consume, where the original nutrients have been damaged, also has a negative effect. Together these force the body, in desperation, to dispose of its waste products in any ways possible. Signs of a problem include a bad smell from the skin pores and the breath. If insufficient waste is removed through these routes, we may develop a cold so that the body can dispose of waste products through phlegm.

Sun breath

This deep breathing technique to relieve tension is essentially one breath, in three stages. Stand with hands by your sides. Breathe into your belly while stretching out your arms. Then breathe into your mid-chest and bring your hands into a prayer position at your heart. Next, lift them over your head and breathe into your upper chest. As you exhale, lower your hands to your sides. Repeat the exercise a couple of times until you feel better.

Hyperventilation is one of the most misunderstood, underdiagnosed, and frequently overlooked illnesses in medicine and psychiatry.

Prof. H.E. Walker

Restricted breathing

There are a number of reasons why we restrict our breathing and start to breathe only in the upper part of the chest. The most common of these are stress and psychosomatic disorders, but it can also have to do with mechanical disorders in the respiratory system or problems in the metabolism that cause changes in the acid-base balance of the blood which needs to be compensated by more rapid breathing. Diabetes and kidney or liver disorders are examples of this. It can also be indicative of disorders in the respiratory centre, or the glands, of a heart condition, high blood pressure and other similar disorders.

But restricted breathing can also be caused by simple problems such as tight clothing, or simply vanity that makes a person walk around with their stomach pulled in — or linked to the food we eat; allergic reactions caused by milk, wheat and corn are some of the most common food-related causes. It has been known for some time that some foodstuffs can cause anxiety, depression, migraine and also hyperactivity and autism in children. There has been an increase in the volume of research to study the links between breathing and the food we eat, and Fried lists a number of products that often affect individuals in this way: they include coffee, tea and carbonated drinks, also cheese, meat, milk products, starch, some fruits and chocolate.[48]

Cure for sea sickness

It is possible to cure sea sickness by changing the breathing pattern. Concentrate on the exhale and make sure it flows without restrictions in an even stream, and that the inhale follows immediately after the exhale. Keeping the breathing even and free-flowing prevents the stomach from contracting in the spasm that causes the nausea. It may help to quietly form the sound *sssssssssssssss* or *mmmmmmmmmm* during the exhale, in order to enhance the free flow of air.

Hyperventilation

The most common breathing disorder is probably hyperventilation. If we don't breath deeply enough to bring in enough oxygen with every breath, we need to breathe more often to compensate. In shallow breathing, the lungs are not given enough space in the chest cavity to expand sufficiently to bring in all the air we need. If we then increase the speed with which we breathe to compensate for this, it can cause the disorder known as hyperventilation. But this means that we will breathe out too much carbon dioxide which in turn may cause imbalance in the acid-base balance of the blood; in order for the body to function optimally the blood needs to be alkaline with a pH level of 7.4.

It is extremely important for the metabolism that the blood has the correct acid-base balance since this has a direct effect on the cells' ability to free and extract oxygen. Even small changes will cause great problems for the cells, and so the body has a special function that monitors and restores any imbalance as soon as possible. When too much carbon dioxide disappears through the exhale and the level in the blood falls below a critical point, this triggers an inhibition of the stimuli to the respiratory centre in the brain which makes us stop breathing. In particular when the hyperventilation disorder is caused by stress or general anxiety, the inability to breathe may lead to an immediate alarm to the body's sympathetic system and cause what we would call a panic attack. If hyperventilation is allowed to continue over a longer period, the body will also adjust the acid-base balance to the lower carbon dioxide level. This may lead to a symptom known as alkalosis which involves cramps and muscular spasms leading to intense pain in both muscles and joints.

Unfortunately the hyperventilation syndrome is surrounded by confusion and misunderstanding. This is partly because the name hyperventilation stands for *hyper* — too much and *ventilation* — the flow or movement of air. But hyperventilation is far from breathing too much, rather it refers to insufficient breathing. A person with insufficient breathing can breathe extensively without bringing much oxygen into the body, whereas a person with a correct breathing pattern can breathe almost invisibly and still bring

Pranayama and carbon dioxide

By inhaling against some resistance (a beanbag or similar weight on the chest) it is possible to increase the carbon dioxide level from around 5.5 per cent to around 6.5 per cent. Inhale for five seconds, pause for 20 seconds, then exhale for 10 seconds. Repeat this six times. The higher level will remain for another four breaths. The main effect, among others, is increased blood flow and a calming effect on the brain.

in more oxygen. What determines the difference is the quality of the breathing, not the amount of air in itself.

The confusion surrounding hyperventilation is reflected in the diagnosis and treatment of this problem. Some disorders such as diabetes can lower the pH value of the blood without changing the carbon dioxide level. Since the respiratory centre can't distinguish this it leads to a faster breathing pattern.

Too little is still known about the effects of incorrect breathing, and it is still common for breathing disorders to remain undetected, or to be incorrectly diagnosed as something that may lead to long term medication or unnecessary medical treatment. For an otherwise healthy person, chronic hyperventilation will often lead to no more than a general lowering of the body functions. But for a person with a heart condition, for example, hyperventilation can be life threatening. It is also common to treat the patient with tranquillizers since the breathing disorder is thought to be caused by psychological disorders that are considered best treated with this type of drug. To make the connection that breathing disorders can cause psychological disorders is still very rare.

The symptoms of hyperventilation are principally increased adrenaline secretion, increased heart-rate and contracted muscles. Hyperventilation also increases the tendency for nose-breathing which leads to irritations on the membranes. In addition, the histamine level in the blood will increase, which leads to increased sweating in the hands and under the arms, and a deeper facial tone. These symptoms usually disappear as soon as the situation that triggered the hyperventilation is resolved.

More serious symptoms of hyperventilation can be irregular heartbeat or chest pain, breathing difficulties, dry cough, dizziness, numbness in fingers and toes, digestive disorders — often irritable bowel syndrome and gases — tiredness, sleep disorders, and also phobia, anxiety and sexual disorders.

It is common for people with chronic breathing disorders to mistake the symptoms for signs of more serious physical problems such as heart attacks, brain tumours or cancer in the stomach. This, in turn, increases the anxiety that may initially cause the hyperventilation, and so the cycle feeds back on itself. It is estimated that as many as thirty and forty per cent of suspected heart attacks are in reality severe symptoms of hyperventilation.

Hyperventilation can also be the cause of a number of psychosomatic disorders such as allergies, anorexia, asthma, cancer, circulatory disorders, diabetes, epilepsy, colds, weakened immune system, heart conditions, skin disorders, headache,

---

Exercising the diaphragm

One way of avoiding the risk of hyperventilation is to exercise the diaphragm. Like any other muscle, it needs exercise to maintain its vigour and functionality. One exercise is to put extra strain on the diaphragm, to 'pump up' the muscle. Lie on your back and place a two kilogram bag (of rice, sand or similar flexible material) between your chest and stomach. Breathe in as normal through the nose, so that the weight on your stomach moves upwards. Breathe out through the mouth so that the weight returns to normal. Repeat this for five to ten minutes. Remove the weight and finish the exercise by breathing normally for a few moments without the weight on the stomach. Repeat this exercise twice a day.

migraine, hypertension (constantly tightened muscles), menstruation disorders, rheumatism and back problems.

It is estimated that around ten to fifteen percent of people in the western world, children as well as adults, suffer from recurring hyperventilation. Some women are more likely to hyperventilate the week before or after their period, and in the last months of pregnancy. One reason is the increased level of progesterone that leads to an increase in the breathing rate. Some women hyperventilate when they give birth, which actually increases the pain and tightens the muscles, so slowing down and complicating the birth process. The most common way of preventing hyperventilation during labour is to teach the mother breathing and relaxation exercises that she can perform during birth.

People with other breathing disorders (in particular asthma) are more likely to hyperventilate. People who suffer from hypertension (that also causes high blood pressure) are also more likely to hyperventilate. This really is a vicious cycle since hyperventilation also causes this type of disorder. Many teenagers suffer from hyperventilation, often caused by high expectations from their family combined with poor self-esteem, poor diet and eating habits, and too little physical activity. Adults in similar circumstances suffer the same risk.

Even fear of flying can actually be a symptom of hyperventilation. Air pressure in the aircraft cabin is a cost factor for the airline, and they perform exact calculations to work out how low the pressure in the cabin can be without causing discomfort for the passengers. Fear of flying is therefore not always necessarily linked with a fear of being high up in the air or in a limited space — the assumed causes of this phobia — but rather instead the body's reaction to lower than normal air pressure. If this is disregarded it can lead to incorrect treatment with tranquillizing drugs, when all that is needed is to make the person aware that they should breathe more deeply and in a more relaxed manner than normal during the flight.

A person who starts to hyperventilate as a consequence of experiencing strong emotions or acute stress will often seek medical advice in the fear of being seriously ill or even dying.

When we can't understand what is happening or what is causing the strong bodily reaction, we often feel as if we are losing control. This can lead to intense anxiety and panic. The medical treatment often consists of preventing and controlling the symptoms. Most commonly this is done with sedatives, by injection of intravenous calcium, and by getting the patient to breathe in the same air as they breathe out. To achieve this the patient either breathes with a paper bag, or the hands, in front of and covering the mouth and nose. This helps to restore the acid-base balance in the blood. But according to Fried this treatment can be as dangerous to the patient as the hyperventilation itself.[49] One reason is that it makes the patient dependent on external assistance instead of learning to come out of the hyperventilation pattern unaided. When, instead, hyperventilating patients are guided through the attack and taught how to restore their normal breathing pattern, this has a positive effect. To show the patient that they can come out of the situation without assistance gives an increased sense of control, which both minimizes the anxiety and the risk of reacting with hyperventilation in the future.

Biting the bullet

During the First World War a common illness was known as 'soldier's heart.' Although the symptoms indicated problems with the heart, this was seldom the case. Instead the real cause was hyperventilation. Some soldiers even discovered that they could develop the symptoms by biting a bullet, which meant that they would swallow some gunpowder. Although gunpowder is in no way harmless to the body, it was considered a way of getting out of the horrors of the war. A reminder of this still lives on in the expression 'to bite the bullet.'[50]

In Holotropic breathwork, we encourage people to begin the session with faster and somewhat deeper breathing, tying inhalation and exhalation into a continuous circle of breath. Once in the process they find their own rhythm and way of breathing.

Stanislav Grof

Superventilation

Since most of the eastern breathing exercises are based on slow and deep breathing, they do not cause hyperventilation. Yet since some of the modern breathing techniques involve more intense breathing, they may cause hyperventilation. In fact the Rebirthing technique is often incorrectly described as a form of hyperventilation. This is because an incorrect breathing pattern during a Rebirthing session may lead to hyperventilation, and if this is not observed and corrected it may even cause cramps (alkalosis). The risk of hyperventilation is highest during the initial Rebirthing sessions when the person is still learning to maintain an open and relaxed breathing pattern throughout the session. A good breathing instructor, however, will know how to avoid hyperventilation by precise instruction of how to increase the relaxation, shortening or lengthening the breaths and how to vary the intensity in the breathing pattern.

Even the correct breathing pattern in Rebirthing is often confused with hyperventilation since it does to some extent resemble 'real' hyperventilation. To mark the difference Rebirthing is sometimes described as 'superventilation.' Unlike hyperventilation, which has a forced exhale, Rebirthing has a relaxed and effortless exhale; this means that the acid-base level remains unaffected. Regardless of the length and the intensity of the breathing pattern, Rebirthing, correctly undertaken, does not lead to 'real' hyperventilation. It may give a tingling sensation throughout the body (as if the blood has become 'carbonated' or fizzy) but despite its intensity it is usually perceived as a positive, indeed quite pleasant, sensation. It is often followed by a sense of deep relaxation throughout the body and can also lead to strong emotional experiences and important mental insights and revelations.

In certain situations superventilation can also lead to contractions of the muscles and even muscle spasms. The explanation given for this is that the intensive breathing pattern dissolves too many psycho-physical energy blockages at the same time, causing a state of temporary imbalance in the body's circulatory systems. The intensified breathing pattern also increases the circulation in areas of the body that have suffered from some degree of restriction. It can be compared with the reaction when the circulation in an arm or a leg has been restricted momentarily. When the flow is re-opened it leads to a tingling sensation until the flow has been rebalanced. Unlike hyperventilation, where it takes time to regain the acid-base level of the blood, the muscle spasms caused by superventilation can disappear instantly. This may coincide with a mental or emotional connection to a re-experienced memory (see also Chapter 2 on Rebirthing). The spasms can disappear completely in one single breath and lead to intense vibrations and tingling throughout the body. These experiences have many similarities with the awakening of kundalini.

In holotropic breathwork the attitude to hyperventilation is different from that in Rebirthing but both techniques recognize the difference between their breathing patterns and 'real' hyperventilation. After collecting data from more than 30,000 people, Stanislav Grof argues that the stereotypical pattern in hyperventilation with cramps in hands and feet is not the same as in holotropic breathwork. Instead he claims that:

> The psychosomatic response to faster breathing, the hyperventilation syndrome, is considered a pathological condition, rather than what it really is, a process that has an enormous healing potential.[51]

Grof too has evidence that it is possible to breathe faster and more intensively for hours without this leading to the classical symptoms for hyperventilation. Instead it will result in increased relaxation, sometimes increased sex-drive or mystical experiences. Even with signs of cramps in hands and feet, continued intensive breathing does not necessarily result in an intensification of the cramps. Instead there seems to be a self-regulatory system in function which 'typically reaches a climactic culmination followed by profound relaxation.'[52] The pattern of this sequence has a certain resemblance to a sexual orgasm. Over time the tensions can move between various parts of the body as their intensity diminishes. The pain caused by the cramps often coincides with a release of painful memories and can lead to powerful insights.

So far, Grof's observations correspond well with those in Rebirthing. The main differences between the various techniques is that Grof (as well as some Rebirthing practitioners) does not draw a linguistic distinction between the breathing pattern in holotropic breathwork (and Rebirthing) and hyperventilation. One factor here can be the unclear definition of hyperventilation. This confusion is a disadvantage for both techniques. Since 'real' hyperventilation has clear negative effects on the body, it is important to avoid it and concentrate on the positive superventilation. Despite this, Grof goes so far as to argue that there is a healing effect in 'hyperventilation' as a result of the intense muscular spasms that may occur as a result.

He claims that we can free ourselves from long term or chronic pain in two ways. One is by catharsis in the form of wild, uncontrolled body movements, coughs, vomiting and so on (a view shared by conventional psychotherapy); the other way is through breathing, which he regards as a new, more efficient and exciting development of psychotherapy. Grof argues that through the breath:

> ... the deep tensions surface in the form of transient muscular contractions of various duration. By sustaining these muscular tensions for extended periods of time, the organism consumes enormous amounts of previously pent-up energy and simplifies its functions by disposing of them. The deep relaxation that typically follows the temporary intensification of old tensions or appearance of previously latent ones bears witness to the healing nature of this process.[53]

Grof compares this with methods used to exercise the body in sports — isotonic and isometric training. During isotonic training the muscular tension stays the same while the length differs (as in boxing). In isometric training the muscle tension varies whereas the length remains the same (as in weight lifting). According to Grof there are many similarities between this type of training and the muscular spasms that can occur in holotropic breathwork. This interpretation is not shared with Rebirthing where the healing effect is ascribed mainly to the chemical process that is triggered by the changed breathing pattern. The increased breathing releases chemical substances that act as information carriers throughout the body and that also contain 'frozen' or blocked memories and emotions. This view is closer to the eastern philosophies that describe breathing exercises as a form of inner cleansing process.

The intricate web of nerves that constitutes the human nervous system weighs only three and a half pounds yet is probably the most complex system known in the universe. And, by the awe and wonderment it produces, it is for some the most beautiful.

Peter Russell

The role of the brain in the breathing process

Of all the body parts, the brain is the most dependent on oxygen and has the largest blood supply. It consumes 25 per cent of the body's oxygen, despite representing only three per cent of the body's total weight. If the oxygen supply decreases, the brain function suffers; and without oxygen it is almost immediately damaged beyond repair.

Conversely, if the oxygen supply increases this has a positive effect. Elderly people suffering from blocked arteries can increase their brain functions dramatically if blood flow through their arteries is restored and, consequently, the oxygen supply is increased. Similarly, treatment in oxygen tents can vitalize the brain of elderly people. This affect is not limited to the elderly; people from all age groups benefit. It is well understood that an increased oxygen supply to the brain increases creativity and logic, and improves the ability to solve problems. Robert B. Livingston, neurosciences professor in California, writes:

> In the adult, the rate of brain activity, measured metabolically, is ten times that of any other tissue in the body at rest. In fact, the brain burns ten times as much oxygen and produces ten times as much carbon dioxide as the rest of the body.[54]

Eastern breathing exercises are based on the assumption that it is possible to influence the mind through the body. By making the breathing more balanced and stable, activity in the brain will automatically become calmer. The inner dialogue that is a continuous process in the brain calms, and reduces in intensity. This reduces oxygen consumption, since the need to maintain a complex thought process is reduced. That then frees up more energy for the rest of the body. Given that oxygen is one of the most important elements in the body's continuing rejuvenation process, this means that the cells of the body get an enhanced ability to repair themselves.

'Cleansing the head' exercise

One *pranayama* exercise is aimed at 'cleansing the head.' It is called *kapalabhati* which means 'luminous skull.' The exercise stimulates the brain activity and leads to 'clearer thoughts.' The breathing cleanses the nose which stimulates the brain. It is described as a kind of reversed breathing pattern that has the same effect as a good laugh. The breathing is faster than normal (through the nose) and without pause between inhale and exhale. This pattern has many similarities with Rebirthing and Holotropic breathwork.

During surgery, it has been observed that the volume of the brain is affected by breathing. Volume decreases during inhalation and increases during exhalation. At a normal breathing rate, the brain moves about 18 times a minute. Faster and more intense breathing acts as a kind of massage for the brain. Increased supply of oxygenated blood also flushes through the brain with a cleansing effect. The capillaries expand and in particular the pineal gland and the pituitary gland are affected.

Breathing into the brain

In the following exercise you can learn to breathe directly into the brain. Become aware of how you breathe and ensure that you involve the whole breathing apparatus. Concentrate on the area between the eyebrows and feel how it becomes softer and more open. When the opening is large enough imagine that you start breathing directly into this area. Make sure you continue to breathe all the way into the belly. Let your thoughts drift freely — observe without analysis. Continue to breathe like this for another 10 minutes before you move the focus of your breathing to the area just below the navel. Become aware of the energy you have stored in this area and continue to breathe like this for another couple of minutes before you finish the exercise.

Understanding the brain

Looking at how the brain works and communicates with its various parts and the rest of the body is important, if we are to understand how the brain influences the mind. The brain is more than the grey mass in our heads. It is also the central nervous system in the spine.

Inside the brain different functions are concentrated in different areas. There are billions of nerve cells that form a network connecting the various functions with each other and the spine. The nerve cells have many dendrites (or fibrous connections) that receive and transmit information in the form of 'chemical messages.' One single cell can contain up to fifty thousand messages and have connections with more than ten thousand other cells, making the total number of connections far too many to calculate. Many cells have long fibres that connect with various parts of the body, and bring information into the brain in a kind of code that is received and analysed by the brain. Despite the complexity of the system and the large number of messages that constantly flow around the body, this communication system works well and in an organized way. Robert B. Livingston comments that 'The brain is like a symphony, well tuned and well disciplined, and it works marvellously. It is always integrated. From the very beginning of embryonic life, it is totally integrated.'[55]

Peptides and opiate receptors

At one time, the brain was regarded as a 'dry' conveyor of electrical impulses. But more recent research has established that it is better described as a 'wet' chemical processor. How communication in the brain works has been studied by many researchers, including Candace Pert who was involved in the discovery of neuro-peptides, a form of amino acid that is produced in the nerve cells and which transmits information in all bodily fluids.

Brain communication can be divided into three different systems, depending on how the information moves around the body. The first is the nervous system (brain, spine and the senses). The second is the endocrine system (hormones). The third is the immune system (spleen, bone marrow, lymph, and the special cells that combat illness). Together they form an intelligent network with communication to and from the brain. One special feature of the immune system is that the cells are not fixed in one specific place, but rather they move around the body depending on where they are most needed. They are not just receivers for neuro-peptides and other chemicals that influence both our health and emotions, they can also produce endorphins (molecules that influence our general wellbeing and therefore sometimes are known as 'happiness hormones').

According to Candace Pert it is impossible to separate the brain's activity from the rest of the body. It is equally impossible to separate the influence of thoughts and emotions from the body functions. She observes that: 'Health is to be a well integrated person that lives in peace with themselves and where all systems cooperate.'[56]

But since medical research does not generally take immeasurable phenomena such as emotions and the soul's activities into consideration, it was the pharmaceutical industry that first showed interest in another of Pert's major discoveries — the opiate receptors. In the search for explanations of how the various parts of medicines react with the body, the opiate receptors were a positive discovery that complemented the theories well.

A receptor is a single body molecule that reacts to energy and chemical signals by vibrating, changing shape, or even giving out a humming sound. According to Pert, the receptors are probably the most elegant and complicated molecules of them all. They are located on the outside of individual cells and act as a form of sensor to monitor everything that happens in the cell's outer environment.

The receptor also acts as a kind of keyhole (or rather combination lock), by merging with the chemical substances (ligands) that send a signal to the receptor to allow access to the interior of the cell. Pert calls this merger a sexual union at the cell level. Depending on what message the ligand conveys, a biochemical chain reaction is triggered that has the ability to change the cell radically, even to the degree of deciding if it is to live or die. It is these reactions on the cellular level that in combination influence the body's activity, both physically and emotionally.

A ligand may consist of an introduced substance (such as medicines) or the body's own substances. There are three different chemical types. The smallest and simplest molecules are the neuro-transmitters which are mainly produced in the brain to transmit information between synapses. The second type is steroids and sex hormones. The third and largest type — comprising around 95 per cent of the total — is the peptides. These play a decisive role for almost all essential life processes, and have such a major impact on emotions, that in her 1997 book of that title, Pert calls them 'molecules of emotions.'

Since the model of the brain as an electrical communication system had been firmly established over time, it was difficult to convince some scientists of the chemical functions. The old theories were so convincing that few saw the need to shift focus.

The old model also gave a different time frame for the development of the brain. The brain functions as previously understood are developed much later in life than the chemical functions, which are developed early in the foetus' development. The body is able to produce peptides such as endorphins long before the brain is formed. Now it is also recognized that the neuro-transmitters that transmit information between the brain synapses, and which were previously seen as so important, have a more limited on/off function than the peptides which can duplicate the neuro-transmitter role, but also move long distances in the body and cause fundamental and complex changes in the cells that they merge with.

The olfactory function

This new research into the body's communication system confirms that the way we breathe can influence the mind. When the focus was on the brain's electrical impulses, there was no direct link between breathing and the brain functions; it was easy to say that the thought process was divided from the rest of the body, and took place only in the brain. But the discovery that 'brain activity' takes place all over the body changes this picture completely. Breathing has a direct influence on body chemistry, which in turn has a direct influence on thoughts, emotions and bodily reactions. We can therefore say that the way we breathe directly influences both our body and our mind.

When we breathe, the olfactory function catches particles in the air that are interpreted as various smells. Although it is not yet established why, we now know that the olfactory function also can activate signals that don't reach us from particles in the air. In other words we can smell things that are not present in our closest environment. The olfactory function has a great impact on our emotions since the nerves from the olfactory function are connected to the part of the brain that controls emotions. This is well understood by the perfume industry — they know that we are willing to spend a lot of money to give out the right signals to influence the emotions of people we meet.

I don't know what you learned from books, but the most
important thing I learned from my grandfathers was that
there is a part of the mind that we don't really know
about and that it is that part that is the most important
in whether we become sick or remain well.

Thomas Largewhiskers,
hundred-year-old Navaho medicine man

The healing potential of the breath

There are many underlying factors for an illness. There are physiological factors, hereditary factors, bacteria and viruses (that is, some form of 'attack' from the outer environment that weakens and disturbs the body's inner functions). In principle the body's own defences — the immune system — are adequate to keep us well, so long as our outer environment is not too destructive. Many studies show that every day we are exposed to attacks from bacteria, and so on, that can make us sick, but which a fully functioning immune system is capable of withstanding.

Another factor behind physical illness is psychological problems. It has been well established that thoughts and emotions play a major role in physical illness. One reason is that psychological problems are often linked with insufficient breathing, which in turn means physiological complications that lead to even less adequate breathing — and so it continues.

Simplified, the interaction between body and mind is as follows: a problem occurs that is experienced as stressful. First to react is the mind that influences the body indirectly through diminished breathing and muscular tensions. If the problem is not solved or noticed at this point, it may lead to a physiological weakening. If the problem still remains unsolved, this weakening can become chronic and/or lead to physical illness. This type of illness is known as psychosomatic. This does not mean, however, that the physical illness 'is all in the mind' as many argue; rather it means that the illness has its origin in a psychological problem that we have been unable to detect and resolve on the mental level, when it was 'all in the mind.' Once the illness has developed it is no different from any other physical illness, which means that it may require medical intervention in the form of drugs or surgery to be eradicated.

A breathing exercise for high blood pressure

If you suffer from high blood pressure the following short exercise may help. According to Deepak Chopra it is more effective than beta blockers (one of the most common drugs for high blood pressure). Breathe in through your nose. Open the jaw and drop the chin down without opening the mouth and breathe out through the nose. It is like when you clean your glasses and breathe on them with a big *haaaaa* to steam them up before you wipe them clean. You breathe the same way here, but with the mouth closed. When the air passes the open space that is formed when you drop the chin you can hear a *haaa*-sound. Repeat the exercise a couple of times and notice how you breathe all the way into the belly and how your body relaxes as a consequence.

If we are to understand how we recover from illness, it is important to establish some of the basic principles for the healing process. First, there are two fundamentally different views on who is responsible for our recovery. One is held by conventional medicine that has made us see the healing process as something done to us by somebody else in a more or less mechanical way. The main factors that determine the success of this process are seen as the quality of the technical and/or pharmaceutical intervention with which we are provided. As clinical patients, we are more or less passive consumers of care.

Massaging the chest muscles

One cause of poor breathing is due to the rib cage losing its elasticity. This is mainly caused by increased rigidity in the muscles that surround the chest. This makes it more difficult for the diaphragm to expand enough to create the cavity that is needed in the chest to bring in sufficient air with each breath. By massaging the muscles in this area their flexibility can be restored, which will lead to improved breathing.

The other view on the healing process is that it is down to each individual to actively take part. Although medical intervention obviously plays a large part, it is ultimately our own body that does the repair work. The patient has the leading role, not the doctors or nurses — their job is merely to assist and facilitate the body's own healing processes. But although research increasingly confirms this view as the more effective route, the prevailing view is still that the doctor is in charge of the healing process, possibly because this best suits the structure of most healthcare systems. Consequently the patient is seen as a passive recipient. As long as the patient follows the instructions everything is fine. What determines the success is the doctor's active effort and the patient's willingness to comply.

The Indian healer and the western healer have a common
denominator — the trust and confidence of both the patient and
the healer. They must both believe in the magic or it doesn't
work. Western doctors make secret markings on paper and
instruct the patient to give it to the oracle in the drug store,
make an offering in return for which they will receive a magic
potion. Although neither understands exactly how the healing is
done, but as long as they both believe, it will work.

Irving Oyle

The placebo effect

Ironically, one of the best proofs of the body's self-healing
ability is a phenomenon that medical research regards as
something of a nuisance. They view it as such since it con-
fuses their results — but they have to live with it, as they
can't find a way to prevent it. This phenomenon is known
as the placebo effect. The word *placebo* is Latin and means
I shall please. It refers to the spontaneous healing process
that regularly takes place, clearly without any help from
effective or other medical intervention. Here I am not refer-
ring to recovery from a cold or other minor ailments, but
rather the spontaneous recovery from serious, even life-
threatening illness.

The placebo effect is most frequently observed and connected with the testing procedure for new drugs. When
evaluating a new medicine, the testing team is required to
assemble a control group alongside the actual test group,
in order to obtain a second set of statistics so results can
be compared between the two groups. The control group
is given 'sugar pills,' water or other completely ineffective
'treatment' — a placebo, prescribed and delivered in
exactly the same way as the real drug. All the patients
know is that they are taking part in a trial of a new drug.
Yet, often, the placebo will duplicate the effect of the powerful drug, despite containing no active ingredients.

What is happening here is that our thoughts are influencing the body chemistry in the same way that the drugs do. This suggests that a drug will react differently depending on our thoughts and emotions when we take it. If a patient believes that a drug is potent, it creates a completely different chemical environment for the drug to that created if the patient believes it to be inefficient or even harmful.

New medicines have been tested in controlled trials of this type for many years and the evidence is clear that it is not the drug itself, but the individual reaction to it, that ultimately decides the success of the treatment. It is even clearly proven that when the control group is given the same information about possible side effects as the group prescribed the potent drug, the pharmaceutically inactive placebo often leads to the same side-effects.

Bizarrely, however, instead of being seen as fantastic evidence of the body's self-healing powers, the placebo effect is regarded as a problem that researchers have to live with. Despite the clear evidence that patients taking completely ineffective placebos can react and recover in exactly the same way as if they were treated with a potent medicine, this is not of interest to the scientists.

Even if 50 per cent of the control group (receiving the placebo), compared to 52 per cent of the test group prescribed potent drugs react positively, the result of the control group is disregarded. The result presented is only the 52 per cent of the test group that indicate a positive reaction to the new drug. (Given that the tests are carried out by the pharmaceutical industry this is understandable, from an economic point of view, although difficult to understand from a wider medical view.) It is estimated that the placebo effect plays a part in between 30 to 70 per cent of all tests.

The nocebo effect

The nocebo effect (from the Latin *nocebo,* I will harm) is the opposite of the placebo effect. That is to say that if we believe that our illness is worse than it actually is, this has a negative effect on the body. A negative effect can make the healing process more difficult and lead to complications.

One contributing factor is that the breathing deteriorates when we are not feeling well emotionally and mentally.

In traditional cultures, where priests and medicine men have a great influence and the tribal identity is deeply rooted, there is clear evidence of the nocebo effect in the form of curses and black magic. In some tribal cultures it is sufficient for the medicine man to put a curse on a member of the tribe, for him/her to fall ill and die, within days — totally inexplicably from a medical point of view. The extent of the nocebo effect in modern medical care has not been measured, but the phenomenon is being noticed and discussed.

> ### Preventing palpitations
>
> Palpitations can be caused by insufficient breathing. One way of preventing this is to increase the exhale. Open the mouth widely and let the air exhale as freely as possible. Make sure not to force the exhale by contracting the muscles in the stomach.

Eminent authorities have stated that one generation of correct breathers would regenerate the race, and disease would be so rare as to be looked upon as a curiosity. Whether looked at from the standpoint of the Oriental or Occidental, the connection between correct breathing and health is readily seen and explained.

Yogi Ramacharaka

Health care or sick care — the western worldview

When the body falls ill it has a deep effect on both body and mind. Whether the underlying cause of the illness is physical or psychological, it creates a state where the joint efforts of both body and mind aren't enough to fight the illness. In reverse, this means that the healing process may involve the very deepest parts of our inner self (or soul) in order to fully restore the body's natural strength. It may involve questioning even the deepest rooted attitudes to life, or thoughts and ideas that we have lived with for so long, that we have come to see them as the very basis of our existence.

To heal the body may also involve mapping a string of incidents that may have led to the current situation. We may need to analyse them one by one and see what impact they have had on us. It can also involve questioning cultural values and the very worldview that our society is based on. An important step may be the realization that this worldview has not always been the same and that what we see as 'objective facts,' merely are the sum of our joint conclusions. Here too, breathing techniques play an important role in helping us to penetrate our inner self to the point where we are able to examine and evaluate our personal history. And, equally important, this may help us to get in touch with the deeper underlying beliefs that form our common western worldview (and that of western medicine).

Although modern western medicine has lost some of its authority, most of us still have great faith in it. Whether we trust it to do a good job or not, most of us still think modern medicine has the ultimate knowledge of the cause and cure of illness. It is in conventional medicine that the western world focuses most of its resources, and one reflection of this powerful position is that most western countries allow medical professionals to act as their own highest authority, and evaluate how good they are at healing people. But has it always been like this? Has it always been the medical doctors that have had exclusive rights to cure ill health? And have the differences between East and West always been as great? In order to fully realize how strong our faith is in western medicine, we have to go back in time and see how the current western situation has evolved, and compare it with the development in other parts of the world.

Countering dizziness

Dizziness in healthy people is often a result of bending forward or getting up quickly. A way of counteracting this is to exhale with a loud haaaa.

Early approaches to healing

Throughout history humans have needed to heal physical illness. That makes the art of healing as old as human history. Thanks to a few remaining indigenous people (that live the same way as we all did in the beginning of history) we have a fairly good idea of the origin of medical care. The methods of healing were very much the same in all parts of the world. To begin with it was shamans and medicine men that had the knowledge and authority to cure illness, and their role was usually a mixture of priest, doctor, magician, exorcist and political leader. They had great authority and were both feared and revered since they could go into trance (reach altered states of consciousness) and communicate directly with gods, spirits and demons that were thought to have huge control over people's everyday life. In order to evoke the trance state they took hallucinogenic herbs and mushrooms, and were helped to reach this state through singing, dancing and drumming. Breathing played an important part and it was possible to reach the 'spirit' world and get (literally) 'in-spired' through 're-spiration.' These visits to the spirit world provided information about the cause and cure of an illness and what herbs could be used in the healing process.

Whether today's extremely mechanistic worldview will be a brief phase in medical history remains to be seen. But compared to the earlier, more holistic approach that was the norm for thousands of years, today's medicine has so far enjoyed a very brief life-span. Modern medicine is said to have its roots in the classic Greek era, when a major healing figure was that of the demi-god Asclepius, or Asklepios (son of the god Apollo and the woman Koronis). His symbol, a rod surrounded by a serpent is said to have the same roots as the Indian symbol for kundalini. To this day it is a medical icon in many countries. In ancient Greece many temples were built to honour Asclepius' healing powers. They also functioned as hospital and holistic healing centres, and were beautifully situated with spas, theatres, and recreational places as well as areas designated for spiritual practices. The treatment included dream therapy known as 'divine sleep,' usually initiated by periods of fasting and mental preparation, and the diagnosis and healing took place in a hypnogogic state of deep relaxation. The Greeks showed great respect for breathing techniques that they regarded mainly as a way of reaching deep relaxation.

Hippocrates, (around 400 BC) was trained in the Asclepian tradition and is regarded as the father of western medicine. He saw the role of the doctor mainly to understand and facilitate the body's natural healing powers, and to establish the patient's relationship to eating and drinking, work and leisure, and to observe the effects these had on the patient. He also applied the art of gentle and loving respect to the healing process.

To this day, physicians all over the world swear a Hippocratic Oath when they graduate and are ready to take up their profession. The classical version starts with the words: 'I swear by Apollo Physician and Asclepius and Hygieia and Panaceia and all the gods and goddesses, making them my witnesses, that I will fulfil according to my ability and judgement this oath and this covenant.'

During the period from AD 500 to 1300, the medical profession in Europe was based on ancient traditions that had many similarities with shamanic healing. Initially all medicine was controlled by the church, but there was also a widespread but more informal approach that was practised by people taught by an older generation. They were known as wise men and women, or sometimes witches and magicians. Both strands of medicine were surrounded by mystical rituals and had a strong religious connection.

In the fifteenth century the physician and founder of modern chemistry, Paracelsus, opened up a new avenue for medical research, consisting in part of re-introducing the old Greek attitude to medicine. He had great respect for the medical tradition based on folklore, and was also the first to make the connection between illness and social environment. As medical progress continued, it became increasingly important to safeguard the social status that was given to healers of all kind. In the sixteenth century this lead to the formation of organizations for physicians and surgeons. One of their first tasks was to bring in laws to establish who was allowed to practise medicine. One group that was banned were the so-called 'quacks' (non-members of the medical organizations). These quacks were often barbers and others with some knowledge of the human body and the healing process, and they worked as unregistered 'amateur surgeons' without formal education. When the big fight for control over the prestigious medical profession started, the quacks lost to the physicians. They were accused of performing magic, or of being insufficiently qualified to practise medicine.

Women usually played an important role in medicine. They had great intuitive powers and knew a lot about the body's natural healing process. But as the new laws were introduced, the church and state intervened and banned them from practicing medicine. The new attitude was that the Christian faith alone was sufficient to cure illness. All medical treatment not based on Christian beliefs was taken to represent the work of the devil. This attitude was later taken to the extreme and women were persecuted and accused of being in league with the devil. In order to protect society from their evil influence, it was not enough to kill them; they had to be burnt alive. These women were said to be able to fly through the air, influence and even kill people at a distance, and to fight demons and evil spirits (something that has also been ascribed to Indian and Tibetan yogis and magicians.) According to Harner, from a modern perspective, the women were a kind of shaman.[57] Like the shamans, many acquired their knowledge in drug-induced states. The drugs were often strong and dangerous and death from overdoses was common. But they did not perform their healing during the drug-induced states. This required a presence that they were not capable of whilst under the influence of drugs.

During the worst witch-hunts, a large number of women in Europe were murdered; between 1500 and 1650 several hundred thousand women are believed to have been killed. Some say the real number was much higher — up to nine million. In the German city of Würzburg, 900 women were murdered during one year. In the French city of Toulouse, 400 women were murdered in one day. In Italian Trier, two villages had only one woman left. The women were accused of causing everything that went wrong in their societies, from the failures of the qualified physicians to cows that stopped milking and the poor crops in the fields. According to a document from 1486: 'all witchcraft comes from carnal lust which is in women insatiable.' *(Malleus Maleficarum)*. A common way of determining if a woman was a witch, was to pull her through water. If she survived she was a witch and was subsequently killed. If she drowned she was innocent (although unfortunately dead). Although we know better now, there is still a certain hesitation against female physicians in many countries.[58]

Science without religion is lame, religion without science is blind.

Albert Einstein

The prevailing western approach

The prevailing western approach to medicine started to form during the seventeenth century, and one of the most important contributions came from the French philosopher René Descartes in the early part of that century. His view became very influential and had a great impact on the modern view on 'scientific facts.' Before Descartes people had different opinions of what the real nature of the world was: some said the world around us is only a part of the true nature of the world, and that it is our mind that limits the full experience. This view was first presented by the Greek philosopher Plato. His student Aristotle argued that our impressions have a physiological impact on us, for instance, when we get angry 'the blood will boil around the heart.' The Italian scientist Galileo, contemporary with Descartes, argued that there are two original substances in the universe — one with a form that can be measured and weighed, and one without a form (a kind of energy) that influences that which has a form. He also divided the world into an objective and a perceived world. But when he also argued that the world revolves around the sun (which of course is our current view) he went a step too far and ended up in a conflict with the Church and sentenced to give up his 'misconceptions.'

Descartes tried to prove the existence of God by pointing at the duality in life. He identified two separate substances — one spiritual and one physical — with different qualities which, by the influence of God, interacted with each other. It is this concept — that the mind is separated from the body and that the outer world is objective and separate from the inner subjective mental world — that since then has been the prevailing view for modern science. For modern medicine Descartes' dualistic worldview meant a great step forward. By differentiating between body and soul it became accepted to examine the body of dead people. (When the soul had left the body all that remained was dead matter, of no interest to the Church.) For western medicine this has become the primary way of exploring the human body.

A hundred years after Descartes first introduced his new ideas, the English mathematician Isaac Newton was the first to describe 'universal' physical laws, including the law of gravity, in works such as the *Opticks* and *Principia Mathematica*. A century after Newton, the English scientist Charles Darwin presented his theory of evolution through natural selection. Darwin's theories have become the foundation stone for modern biology and anthropology.

One consequence of Descartes' worldview was the mis-

conception that a scientist's role is to 'detect natural phenomena floating around in our universe' waiting to be discovered. Up until the beginning of the twentieth century the
new worldview proved itself effective since science dealt
with measurable objects in the 'outer' visible world. But following the arrival of new theories (above all in quantum
physics) with new investigative tools, the prevailing worldview has started to show signs of inadequacy.

According to Thomas Kuhn the definition for 'conventional
science' is that the role of the scientist is 'puzzle-solving within
an unquestioned paradigm.'[59] In other words it is not the scientist's job to question the current worldview, but rather to
focus on how the results coincide with other discoveries
within the same worldview. For instance, the current scientific worldview, or paradigm, states that a human being has
five senses. But since this view separates between inner (subjective and consequently 'unscientific') and outer (objective
and consequently 'scientific'), neither consciousness nor soul
are afforded a place in science. These are assigned to the
domain of religion — that which deals with issues concerning faith (that is, unscientific issues). As a consequence, new
insights are constantly dismissed by the scientific establishment simply because they do not fit into their scientific
worldview. One way of defining 'unscientific' discoveries is
to term them as 'paranormal' (that is, inexplicable), and as a
consequence they fall outside the working field of the scientific establishment. This view still rules the scientific establishment today — but that is not to say that this view is
shared by all scientists: the number of scientists worldwide
who question this is growing. One significant reason is that
more and more intriguing results are being obtained from
conventional and scientifically stringent research methods in
'unscientific' areas. In reality, the need for a paradigm shift is
growing so quickly that a change is unavoidable, or the
integrity of the entire scientific establishment will be questioned. In the emerging worldview that is gradually replacing
the current scientific paradigm, science and research are seen
more as ways of creating mental models of how the universe

works. The engineer and researcher Arthur Ellison observed: 'Science is a process of building mental representational models patterning and ordering our mental experiences.'[60] In other words there is a growing recognition that what we call 'objective facts' in reality only are our mental constructions. Paradoxically this leads back to Descartes, who also declared that all he really could be sure of was that his thoughts were the only proof of his existence. So his famous expression *Cogito, ergo sum* (I think, therefore I exist) — a statement that has been one of the cornerstones for the current world-view — can also fit into the emerging worldview (even if Descartes did not see it that way).

Western development has encouraged us to see the world as predictable, and argued that with sufficient knowledge it is possible to figure out absolutely everything in nature with mathematical precision. For obvious reasons, subjective experiences and emotions have no place in this world. To describe beauty in a scientific way means listing all the physiological activities in the body and brain, which cells are activated, which hormones are secreted and so on yet, despite this, we all know that this does not describe how we experience beauty.

The body machine

Our materialistic worldview has made us see the human being as a machine with exchangeable parts. Many still live as though their body functions are unaffected by their lifestyle and external environment. To cure illness, it is merely a question of detecting and inhibiting, or reversing symptoms, and nothing at all to do with the rest of a person's inner and outer life.

When the body is seen as a machine, it is a natural consequence that transplants and organ donations are the focus of the medical debate. Instead of respect and support for the body's own ability to restore and heal, vast amounts of money are spent on methods to replace body parts that have stopped performing adequately.

Gene manipulation is another example of medical

research 'at its best.' Scientists are fighting fiercely to be the first to map the gene bank so that they can patent their discovery and make large sums of money from controlling the healing process for others.

Many see gene manipulation as the future of medicine. Yet at the same time, others argue that it is wrong to ignore and override the body's natural functions, that for millennia have proven that the body has a natural ability to restore itself, and that this facility is as powerful, even more powerful, than any outer manipulation.

For many Darwin's evolution theories indicate that humans have a special role as the highest creation in nature. Therefore it is seen as ethically acceptable to artificially produce animals (cloning) to use them as spare parts for humans in need of transplant organs. Some scientists try to extend the limits even further by trying to create human clones. At the same time, critics argue that this is both unethical and dangerous since we still know much too little of how our universe really works.

The continuing development of medicine should not be about dismissing or diminishing the importance of stringent research methods of the highest quality. What is needed is a questioning of the prevailing scientific paradigm, and the bringing in of new ways of conducting research. Control groups and blind tests (required in current research methods) are not a good way to establish the body's natural healing ability. To study functions that are influenced by the patient's inner faith and conviction, and are the result of a close and intimate interaction between patient/therapist demands different research methods. To dismiss phenomena simply because it is not possible to measure them with current research methods is to dismiss volumes of anecdotal evidence from people who firmly believe that they have been able to heal themselves without medical intervention. This is a fact that established science will have to accept. At the same time alternative healing methods or complementary medicine on their part need to overcome a reluctance to accept that hard data and scientific stringency are sometimes necessary to prove that a method is sound. As so often, a balanced view must be the final goal.

Above: the heavens — sky, sun, stars, moon, planets.
Below: the elements — space, air, fire, water, earth.
From these: the body — shape and form, vital breath,
digestive fire, blood and water, skeleton and flesh.
And the senses — hearing, touch, sight, taste, smell.
In contemplation of these sets of five,
The wise discovered that all things are holy.
One can complete the inner with the outer.

Taittiriya Upanishad

Traditional Eastern medicine

Traditional eastern medicine evolved from a basically subjective worldview: the knowledge accumulated from subjective observations of the human body and reflections from meditation. According to the Vedanta worldview (a system of Hindu philosophy based on the holy books called the *Vedas)*, everything has its origin in the mind, and everything is controlled by the mind. The world around is in effect an illusion of the mind. Unlike western medicine, the knowledge is built on observations of living bodies rather than dissection of dead bodies. They are therefore able to identify a circulatory system for the body's energy, how the life energy enters the body and circulates throughout it. This principle is totally unrecognized in western medicine. The many Asian countries share the same basic view although the various concepts and more detailed descriptions vary somewhat.

India

Ayurvedic medicine in India has been practised for around three thousand years. The term *Ayur-Veda* is Sanskrit and consists of the words *Ayur* (health/life) and *Veda* (knowledge). The first knowledge is said to come from the Indian

Veda-scriptures. Most likely its development has been gradual and the religious connotations have been added during this process.

Originally theories about illness were divided into two broad areas: first, attacks from demons (in the West these would be described as psychomatic illnesses), which would be cured by a combination of prayers and mantras to exorcise the demons. Second, superficial illness, best treated with herbs and minor surgical intervention. To begin with, all treatment involved a combination of magic and rituals, but today Ayurvedic medicine also includes nutritional advice as well as general advice on health, exercise and mental and physical cleansing methods such as yoga and breathing exercises *(pranayama)*. In the earliest Ayur-Vedic scriptures (around 2000 years old) pathology, diagnosis and treatment (including surgical intervention) are described as well as philosophy and general advice for how to maintain health. Some texts are very detailed. They spread at an early stage to Europe, above all to Greece, and also to the Arab countries.

Tridosha

Ayurvedic medicine is based on the five original elements: ether, air, fire, water and earth. Together they form the base for *tridosha* — the three elements *vata* (air), *pitta* (bile) and *kapha* (phlegm) which unite the human body with the cosmic forces. The air *(prana)* has a dominant place. *Prana* influences all the bodily functions and is divided into various functions. *Apana* influences the areas around the anus, in a downward movement and controls among other things urine and faeces and the sexual organs. *Samana* influences the area around the navel and controls among other things the digestive system. *Udana* influences the area around the neck and controls — among other functions — speech. *Vyana* influences all parts of the body. Illness occurs when one element gets out of balance with the others.

Body and breath, essence and energy are one
when the body does not move, essence cannot flow
when essence cannot flow, energy stagnates.

Sun Ssu-Mo, Taoist Physician

China

The Taoist system is based on two principles *yin and yang*. These are opposites — dynamism and effect, expansion and contraction. Together they form all phenomena in the universe. It is the balance between yin and yang that is illustrated in the Chinese symbol that is well known in the western world today.

There are three main principles that control the universe:

1) The yin force attracts the yang force in order to reach a state of balance. This is reflected in all situations where forces attract each other, from magnetic fields to sexual attraction.
2) Forces of the same kind repel each other to give place to opposite forces to unite.
3) Too much yin or yang leads to a change to the opposite force. This is reflected in the human life cycle — birth, old age, death and rebirth and the seasonal changes.

According to traditional Chinese medicine, illness is caused by imbalance between body and mind (as for psychomatic illness). The body's yin and yang forces are out of balance. The outer environment plays an important part in diagnosis and cure of illness. Imbalance between a person and the elements in the outer environment can lead to illness.

All life is created from the interaction between the five elements, wood, fire, earth, metal and water, which influence each other in a perpetual dynamic life-cycle. In order to restore the body, any imbalance has to be addressed. To establish where this imbalance is strongest, the diagnosis consists of a thorough investigation of the patient's lifestyle and diet. In addition healers use a very sophisticated system of analysing pulse and urine. The treatment (just as with the Ayurvedic medicine) can consist of breathing exercises, acupuncture, nutritional advice and general advice on how to restore the body's balance. In traditional Chinese medicine, the physician's role is to keep the patient well. If he has to treat an illness this is a sign that he has not done his job well, and in earlier days this would mean that he would not get paid. The patient was only willing to pay the doctor for the time he was kept well.

Lung'ta of breath, of body, of power,
may you increase and grow like the new moon.
Print from a Tibetan woodcut.

Traditional Tibetan medicine

The traditional Tibetan medicine is called *sowa rigpa*. It originates from the Buddhist and Ayur-Vedic medicine that was introduced to Tibet during the second century AD from monasteries in northern India. Tibet's first medical school was built in the eighth century. The Indian influence lasted till the seventeenth century. Tibetan medicine has also been influenced by China, Iran and Greece. For a long time Tibet was isolated from the rest of the world. It was not until the Chinese invasion in the 1950s that knowledge of Tibet started to spread outside the country.

There is no clear distinction in Tibetan medicine between religion and medicine: instead human existence is divided into three different aspects — *Dharma* stands for the religious aspect; *Tantra* stands for various cleansing methods for body and mind; and the *Somatic* aspect stands for the medical care. The main cause of all illness is that a person is not aware of the full truth in life. The full truth is that everything in life is volatile and in constant change, and that human beings are filled with desires, have a tendency to hang on to their thoughts, and are controlled by emotions and mental confusion. These three negative states are known as the three poisons, and their influence creates imbalance in the body that causes illness (psychosomatic). The first poison is illustrated with a bird: this stands for envy and pride and leads to impatience at the same time, as it causes problems with the mind and the breathing. The second poison is symbolized by a snake: this stands for anger, disapproval and aversion and causes problems with the eyes and digestion. The third poison is symbolized by a pig: this stands for mental inactivity and incorrect thoughts and leads to a general stiffness in the body as well as digestive problems.

Illness is also divided into categories related to problems in the patient's life. The first group has its origin in the earliest part of our life, and can be caused by a mother's difficulties during pregnancy, or through poor diet early in life. The second group has its origin in the patient's current life situation. It can be the general lifestyle, diet or conduct. The third group has its origin in karma from earlier lives — bad actions in a previous life can come back and have a negative influence in this life. The fourth group has its origin in the spirit world. It can involve a conscious or unconscious lack of respect for the spiritual world in thoughts and actions.

Part of the diagnosis in traditional Tibetan medicine is to

Kum nye exercise

Kum nye is a type of self massage that is often prescribed by Tibetan physicians. It is aimed at increasing the balance and relaxation in the body. Here is a short example:

Stand up and place the right arm over the left arm with each hand on the opposite shoulder. Cross the right leg over the left leg with both feet on the ground, so that you are standing cross-legged. Hold this posture and start breathing deeply and slowly for a short while. Change sides — to left over right — and repeat the exercise. Notice how the energy starts to move in the other side of the body. This posture balances both the body's energy and the brain function. Continue the exercise by holding your arms straight out from the body. Stand with your feet slightly separated and the soles flat on the floor. Focus your attention on the heart and try to visualize how body energy is radiating out and down along your arms. Bring in your hands so that they meet in front of the heart. Repeat the whole exercise a couple of times and notice how the energy flows in the body.

interpret dreams and omens. This increases the understanding of underlying factors for an illness which helps to establish how the illness is best treated. Since dreams can be caused by imbalance in the body they help to indicate where the imbalance is greatest. An important way to restore inner balance is to use various breathing techniques.

When the nadis are purified by nadishodhana pranayama
the prana enters sushumna with a force,
and the mind becomes calm.
Shandilyopanishad 1.7.10

Eastern theories on healing

When western science separated the body from the soul
and declared the soul 'unscientific,' it became much easier
to study the body's physiological functions since it was
now permissible to dissect dead bodies. But the study of
dead bodies did not reveal how the body's energy moves
inside us when we are alive. The only circulatory systems
revealed by dissection were for the body's fluids.
Consequently, explaining life energy was never an issue.
But in the East, where the body and soul were never separated, medical knowledge has always been based on the
study of live bodies. Here an additional circulatory system
was identified — the circulation of the body's 'internal
energy.'

Despite the differences between these eastern and western perspectives, we can now begin to see a convergence.
eastern medical ideas may still be very alien to western scientists in general, but recent research indicates that eastern
knowledge provides a very accurate account of the body's
metabolism and processing of internal energy. A view commonly shared both in the East and West, is the differentia-
tion between the physiological and psychological functions.
All eastern schools agree on this and differ only in details.
According to the yoga school the human body has five functions or 'bodies': the physical body, the energy or pranic
body, the mental body, the intuitive mental body and the
bliss body. This structure is designed to illustrate the body's
ability to absorb life energy. In order to benefit from life
energy it is essential to breathe fully so that all five bodies
remain open and receptive. This leads to the 'inner breathing' that repairs and revitalizes the body and mind. Yoga
exercises are a way to fine-tune the body's functions and
make them more susceptible to the inner breath.

Both East and West agree that the physical body is surrounded by an electromagnetic energy field. In India, this is
known as the aura (which is the expression most commonly
used in the West). Western science now indicates that all liv-

ing beings in the universe are surrounded by an energy field, although it is yet not clear what its function is. In the East the aura is said to reflect the body's physical and mental state (a person's characteristics or personality). One of the functions of the aura is to trap the outer supply of life energy and bring it into the body. The outer supply comes from sunlight, prana and the earth's natural electromagnetic radiation.

> *There is an endless net of threads throughout the universe. The horizontal threads are in space. The vertical threads are in time. At every crossing of the threads, there is an individual. And every individual is a crystal bead. And every crystal bead reflects not only the light from every other crystal in the net, but also every other reflection throughout the entire universe.*
>
> Rig Veda

The Chakra system

The body's inner energy is circulated through a system consisting of around 70,000 energy channels. In India they are known as *nadis*. In China they are called *ching luo or meridians*. The channels have seven cross-points (the number varies between different schools depending on how they are grouped). They are placed along the spine, from its base to the crown of the head. They are known as *chakras*. The word *chakra* means wheel and refers to the wheel-like whirlpool of energy which is formed at the cross-points. Each chakra is a vortex of energy. The current between the different chakras creates a counter-flow. This forms the aura. Each chakra vibrates at a certain frequency which is reflected in the human psyche and experienced as levels of consciousness. The chakra points correspond to the body's major glands. Western science describes the glands as kinds of relay station for the body's information molecules. Given that information molecules also contain emotions and thought in chemical form, this description corresponds well with the eastern theory of different levels of consciousness.

The lowest chakra, at the base of the spine, is known as the first chakra. It is concerned in its mental aspect with personal safety. The seventh, or the highest chakra, reflects a sense of enlightenment and cosmic union. It is possible to be unbalanced in a certain chakra only, and this will be expressed in behaviour. An imbalance in the first chakra, for example, will make a person largely concerned with personal safety. People may have reached different levels of balance for various areas in life, especially those who have developed specific talents.

The chakra system is not unique to the eastern cultures. Christianity initially had a similar theoretical structure which had clear similarities with the chakra system. The Christian sacraments, that still play an important role in most western countries, are based on these initial theories. Another source of great religious importance, the traditional Hebrew text known as the Kabbalah's *Tree of Life,* also has many similarities with the chakra system. Kabbalah is an aspect of Jewish mysticism that speculates on the nature of divinity, the creation, the origin and fate of the soul, and the role of human beings. It consists of meditative, devotional, mystical and magical practices, taught only to a select few. The eastern chakra system is now gaining recognition in the West, mainly because of the increasing interest in yoga, martial arts and eastern philosophies in general.

Below is a summary of the chakra system. To illustrate the comparisons between the eastern and western views, Dr Caroline Myss' explanations are added as well as explanations from the Kabbalah and Christian rituals.[61] Caroline Myss is an American woman who has developed the ability to diagnose physical illness by intuitive means. She has worked closely with conventional western medical practitioners for many years and her ability to detect the factors underlying a person's physical illness is well established statistically. (Please note however, that the physical disorders mentioned below merely indicate tendencies and an increased vulnerability to a certain illness, rather than indicating specific illnesses.)

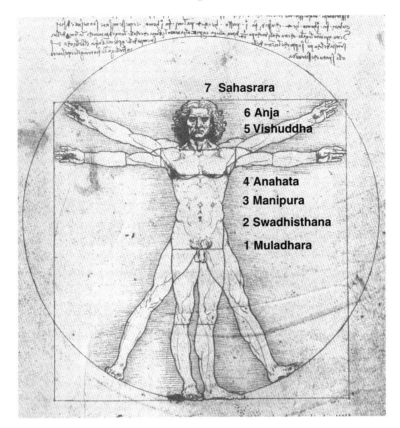

1. MULADHARA (Root Support, the Wheel of Fortune) linked with personal safety.

Eastern explanation: Balance gives a sense of inner safety.

Location: At the base of the spine. It corresponds to the pelvic plexus, testes and ovaries.

Correspondence in Christianity: Baptism.

Correspondence in Kabbalah: Shekinah (mystical community of humanity).

Physiological connection: Rectum, spine, legs, feet and immune system.

Mental and emotional connection: Need for logic, order and structure.

Problems: Fear of death, abandonment and of chaos in the outer environment.

Openness: Can give a sense of belonging to family and

society, sense of common pride and loyalty, sense of security, being linked with the physical world.

Disorders: Chronic lower back pain, varicose veins, depressions, immune-related disorders.

2. SWADHISTHANA (One's Own Place, The Wheel of Change) linked with personal and sensual pleasure.

Eastern explanation: Balance decreases the need for personal and sensual pleasure.

Location: Just below the navel. It corresponds to the hypogastric plexus, adrenal glands and kidneys.

Correspondence in Christianity: Communion

Correspondence in Kabbalah: Yesod — God's creative power

Physiological connection: Large intestine, pelvis hip, appendix, bladder

Mental and emotional connection: Need for contact with others and our need to control the outer environment (being respected, money and physical needs).

Problems: Fear of losing control, fear of being controlled by addiction, sexual abuse, impotence, loss of money or relationships.

Openness: Can give a sense of ability to provide for life's necessities, sense of independence, ability to stand up for oneself, to take risks and to get through personal crisis.

Disorders: Prostate and ovarian cancer, urinary problems, chronic lower back and hip pain, rheumatism.

3. MANIPURA (Gem City) linked with drives for power.

Eastern explanation: Balance gives balance of internal and external power.

Location: Just above the navel. It corresponds to the solar plexus, liver and pancreas.

Correspondence in Christianity: Confirmation

Correspondence in Kabbalah: Hod (God's majesty) and Nezah (God's endurance).

Physiological connection: Stomach, kidneys, gallbladder.

Mental and emotional connection: Personal strength and power, personality and ego.

Problems: Linked with personal responsibility, self-esteem. Can lead to sensitivity of criticism, fear of failure and fear of not being accepted (feeling ugly, fat, or too old).

Openness: Good self-esteem and self-discipline, ability to initiate activity and handle crises, willingness to take risks, generosity and generally strong character.

Disorders: Gastric ulcers, colon/intestinal problems, diabetes, indigestion, liver dysfunction.

4. ANAHATA (The Unstruck Sound, The Wheel of Phenomena) develops creativity and love.

Eastern explanation: Balance gives a sense of unconditional love.

Location: The heart region. It corresponds to the cardiac plexus and thymus gland.

Correspondence in Christianity: Marriage

Correspondence in Kabbalah: Tif'eret — the symbol of compassion, harmony and beauty.

Physiological connection: Heart and circulatory system, lungs, diaphragm, arms and hands.

Mental and emotional connection: Our emotional power, our ability to express emotions and create a stable inner emotional state of mind.

Problems: Fear of loneliness and difficulties in protecting emotions, can lead to jealousy, bitterness, resentment, hate and inability to forgive.

Openness: Love, willingness to forgive, compassion, faith and ability to heal.

Disorders: Congestive heart failure, asthma, allergies, lung cancer, breast cancer.

5. VISHUDDHA (Purity Centre, The Wheel of Happiness) integrates events.

Eastern explanation: Balance leads to inner harmony.

Location: In the throat area and corresponds to the pharyngela plexus and thyroid gland.

Correspondence in Christianity: Confession

Correspondence in Kabbalah: Gevurad (judgement) och Hesed (God's love and mercy).

Physiological connection: Throat, thyroid, trachea, oesophagus, parathyroid, hypothalamus, neck, vertebrae, mouth, jaw, teeth.

Mental and emotional connection: Mental and emotional efforts to make the right choice.

Problems: Fear of making decisions. Since our personal will is involved in most everyday activities, all forms of illness have some connection to this chakra.

Openness: Increased trust, personal authority and the ability to make decisions and stand by them.

Disorders: Raspy throat, chronic sore throat, mouth ulcers, joint problems.

6. AJNA (Non-Knowledge)

Eastern explanation: Balance can give Siddhi or supernatural powers (ESP).

Location: Between the eyes — third eye — corresponds to the naso-ciliary plexus and the pituitary gland.

Correspondence in Christianity: Ordination

Correspondence in Kabbalah: Binah, God's understanding and intelligence and Hokhmah, the contact between divine knowledge and human thought.

Physiological connection: Brain, neurological system, pituitary and pineal glands, eyes and nose.

Mental and emotional connection: Intelligence and psychological profile — a combination of what we know and what we think we know, and a mixture of facts, fears, personal experiences and memories.

Problems: Can lead to unwillingness to find answers within ourselves, fear of hearing the truth and fear of trusting others.

Openness: Can give clear intellect, inspiration, intuition and creativity, emotional intelligence.

Disorders: Brain tumour, stroke, blindness, deafness, learning disabilities.

7. **SAHASRARA** (The Thousand-Petaled Centre or The Unqualified Absolute) is the union of all levels of consciousness with the highest.

Eastern explanation: Balance here unites all levels of consciousness with the highest awareness and leads to enlightenment.

Location: Top of the skull. Corresponds to the cerebrum and the pineal gland.

Correspondence in Christianity: Extreme unction

Correspondence in Kabbalah: Keter — the symbol of the divine that takes physical form.

Physiological connection: Central nervous system, muscular system, skin.

Mental and emotional connection: Dedication, inspiration and mystical insights. (Spiritual experiences belong in this chakra whereas religion belongs to the first chakra.)

Problems: Can give a sense of lost identity and contact with the rest of the world and religious doubts.

Openness: Can give a strong sense of inner guidance.

Disorders: General tiredness, inexplicable depression, extreme sensitivity to sounds, light and other disturbances in the environment.

Opening of the chakras

When the kundalini energy (the latent life-energy) is activated, the process normally starts in the lowest chakra. The energy continues upwards towards the highest chakra (also known as the crown chakra). When it has reached the top of the head it turns down again, over the face, through the throat until it reaches the lower abdomen, where it finally stops. This process usually takes place over a long period (several years). Still the power can be so concentrated that the physical sensation of energy moving in the body is clearly noticeable, in particular when it reaches blockages in the internal energy flow. When the energy encounters blockages, they are, according to yoga theory, dissolved in the form of 'blocks of impurity or karma' and discharged with the rest of the body's waste products. The kundalini energy can move in several directions simultaneously and dissolve blocked energy in several areas. This increases the circulation and forces the communication channels in the cerebrospinal system (brain and spine) to expand. This gradual change makes it possible for consciousness to expand beyond its normal limitations. The kundalini energy may become stagnate on a new level, in particular in the blocked areas.

The physical reactions of people who are undergoing experiences of spontaneous healing, have been found to have many similarities with the activation of kundalini. According to Achterberg a number of recorded cases of unexpected and spectacular self-healing have revealed experiences of intense heat, bubbling (as if the blood is carbonated), a sense of numbness or itching in the area of the illness.[62] These are signs of increased activity in the immune system. Many describe images of a pleasant sense of warmth, as being filled with white light. Others describe an incandescent globe hovering over the body, just before the healing took place. Many had mental images of the body being healed. People with real knowledge of the physical healing process showed signs that this had a positive effect.

Another important detail in spontaneous healing is to have dreams and mental images of the healing process just before falling asleep (hypnagogic images). This often indicates that the healing process has been initiated (a kind of mental knowledge that the body is about to be healed). The images often provided deep insights into the illness and these later had a great impact on the subsequent healing. How well a person can interpret their images has a direct impact on the healing process. The images are often symbolic and preverbal. This indicates that they are associated with experiences in early childhood before the patient had learned to speak. When patients have had a chance to interpret the images in a safe and positive environment, this has had a remarkable effect on the healing process. This interpretation process is best carried out while lying down. This helps to deactivate the parts of the brain that control body movements and prevent them from interfering with other brain activity. As part of the interpretation it is useful to ask questions concerning how the illness is related to the patient's outlook on life and general lifestyle, and if anything has happened that relates to their current situation or has created a sense of their life being less meaningful.

Problems cannot be solved at the same level of awareness that created them.

Albert Einstein

Modern western medical care

There is a growing interest in healing methods that involve breathing in modern medicine. An obvious reason is that it offers a very inexpensive alternative (a factor of great importance in many countries with ageing populations and escalating costs for healthcare). Many alternative forms of medicine (many of which include breathing exercises) are also better at treating some disorders than conventional medicine. Conventional medicine's strength is in treating clearly defined acute illnesses and illnesses which require surgical intervention. Less well-defined illnesses, such as circulatory problems, pains and a general deterioration of body functions, cause much more of a problem. One reason is the lack of time and resources allocated to finding the underlying causes of an illness. This often leads to a situation where symptoms are treated whereas their underlying cause remains undetected. As a result, the disappearance of one symptom often leads to the appearance of another as these are simply the outer signs of the same underlying illness.

Treating illness with medicines makes it possible to reduce consultation periods to a couple of minutes per patient. Short term, this is a cost-effective solution. But the number of re-occurring illnesses in patients who are unable to work for long periods undermines the short-term cost benefits. Medicines also have their problems. Drugs that have been regarded as safe and effective and have been pre-scribed for many years have started to display previously unknown long-term side-effects. One such example is the extensive use of antibiotics. They have been used both to cure human illness and preventively by animal breeders supplying our food chain. This has led to many antibiotics losing their potency due to resistant bacteria.

Another important factor behind the interest in new treatments is that the authorities in many countries face serious problems with providing adequate care for their elderly. In the USA, for example, alternative health care that will lead to better health in older people, is one of the greatest areas of medical research. Even extreme solutions are investigated in a rather desperate search for ways of cutting the costs of medical care.

Caroline Myss clearly shows how imbalance in the body's energy centres can lead to physical illness.[63] Her intuitive method has also shown that it is not always necessary to examine the physical body in order to diagnose an illness correctly. But above all she shows the strong connection between body and psyche and the importance of tracing underlying causes. If it is possible to establish the real cause of energetic imbalance, this offers the best chance of a permanent positive change. This is an area with one of the greatest potential for breathwork. Breathwork allows the person to get in touch with the absolute starting point in their life and re-experience all that may be a contributing factor to their current situation.

The more pressure put on modern medicine, the more willing it has become to integrate alternative approaches. Today it is common in many countries to recommend yoga, meditation and breathing exercises as a remedy for stress. There is also a growing awareness of the importance of a calming and positive environment to facilitate and shorten the recovery period. Music and self-hypnosis or affirmations have also been recognized as having a positive effect on the healing process. Experiments to try to initiate the healing process by describing exactly how this process will take place in the body, when the patient is still in the oper-

> ## A personal experience
>
> The first time I had a general anaesthetic I woke up with an unpleasant feeling of having lost my memory. It had nothing to do with the operation itself. It was quite uneventful. But I felt as if I was missing a short period of my life, in a vague and inexplicable way. It was an irritating feeling which I could not get rid of. As if by some misguided sense of greed I felt very strongly that I wanted to get my lost time back. When I, a couple of months later, did a Rebirthing session I suddenly experienced myself in a dream-like sequence, being back on the operation table. In a detached way I saw and heard what was happening around me. There was nothing particularly dramatic happening, but afterwards the feeling of a time-gap in my mind had gone completely.

ating theatre have also been attempted. Studies have confirmed that the patient can register events during an operation and later describe this with the help of hypnosis. The impressions have been registered in the brain, outside consciousness. Patients that were given this kind of positive feedback have had a shorter and less problematic recovery.

An increasing number of disorders are being regarded as psychosomatic. Not only disorders such as eczema, asthma, sexual organ dysfunctions, anorexia, alcoholism but also cardiovascular disease, high blood pressure and other stress-related disorders. In the USA, both heart attacks and high blood pressure are classified as epidemic disorders due to their rapidly increasing number. The medical definition of stress is a physiological dysfunction — a hypermetabolism — that increases the energy level, body temperature and blood pressure in combination with muscular tension. Statistics from regular health checks show that it is common for middle-aged people to have an increased heart rate and pulse, with a considerable impact on their general wellbeing and longevity. Younger people tend to manage stress by compensating this with the extra energy that the body requires. But later in life the energy supply decreases as more and more body energy gets blocked by the stress. This can lead to excessive production of hormones, too much use of vital body energy to maintain hormone levels and muscle tension, blockage in the circulatory system, increased pressure on internal organs and restricted secretion of bodily fluids. Together this leads to increased wear and tear on the body which makes the ageing faster. Since the real causes of stress often are complex and remain undetected, stress often leads to a sense of longing for some kind of change. This feeling may be vague and general. This often makes us eat, drink or smoke too much in an attempt to compensate.

Another area with increased potential for breathwork is cancer. The connection between cancer and emotions has been known for several hundred years. But it is not until lately that experts have started to agree that suppressed emotions, above all anger and sadness can cause problems for the immune system. Since stress also leads to hormonal imbalance, both these factors can contribute to an increase of abnormal cells. To be able to access and deal with underlying causes for stress through breathwork therefore opens up to an increased healing potential.

The fact that the body is inextricably tied to the soul, and hence its illness may find their source and their cure in the spirit has been described by many cancer patients. A woman journalist has given a vivid account of her experience of being diagnosed as having cancer and her struggle to come to terms with her illness and her new situation:

> To have cancer is like being pregnant with a monster that has to be aborted — therefore it hurts to get rid of cancer. You cannot, in my view, simply rely on one single school, or alternative medicine to cure you. Everything that helps hurts. It takes a tremendous struggle. I have never before experienced such a connection between body and soul. If you have pain in

your soul, you will eventually get all the disharmony that you feel in the soul to be expressed in the cancer. You cannot get rid of cancer without, in some way, also getting straight with your soul.[64]

Our body and mind are not two, and not one.
If you think your body and mind are two, that is wrong;
if you think that they are one, that is also wrong.
Our body and mind are both two and one.

Shunryu Suzuki

Breathwork and modern psychology

In order to understand how underlying factors can lead to psychological and psychosomatic illness, it is necessary to understand how the mind works. Modern psychology has contributed greatly to this task, in particular the fairly new area of psychobiology which looks at how human evolution has formed us into the beings we are today. The result has been to discover that much of what has been regarded as psychological or physical 'malfunctioning' is in reality a sign of a healthy body's reaction to a 'malfunctioning' environment.

Understanding how the human brain evolved can help to explain why breathwork can have such deep and positive effect on our body and mind. The evolutionary process gradually gave us the increased brainpower which makes us unique as a species. This has not led to an unambiguous improvement in the quality of our subjective lives; with our ability to draw conclusions and learn from past experiences has come our tendency to worry about the future. And as a result we are able to influence the body, both consciously and unconsciously and in both positive and negative ways.

Interestingly, our breathing pattern seems to have played an important role in the development of our superior brainpower. According to some scientists our ability to sweat has had a major impact on the development of the brain and consequently of our species. Unlike other mammals, we don't use the breath to cool us down, as our body is cooled down by sweat. This means that we don't need to pant in order to keep cool. This has 'freed-up' the structure of the human windpipe, enabling the complex evolutionary development of verbal expressions which eventually led to modern language. This, in turn, generated a need for increased brainpower, which, as we know, was very successful in evolutionary terms.

As a species, *Homo sapiens* has been extremely successful. From being one among many species, we have now come to dominate the planet. One of the main factors behind this success is the performance of our large and advanced brain, one of the best protected organs in our bodies. One defence mechanism that protects the brain is called the autonomic nervous system. Its job is to filter the impressions registered by our various senses, to ensure that they don't overwhelm the brain.

The autonomic nervous system has two different functions — one sympathetic and the other parasympathetic. The sympathetic system activates the body's defence system. It mobilizes and alarms the body; raises pulse and blood pressure, increases urine secretion, and releases stress hormones. The result is impulsive and outward-oriented behaviour; the muscles contract and the breathing pattern becomes shallower, and higher up in the chest. This impedes impressions from the outer world penetrating too deeply into the consciousness where they could cause disorientation and distract attention from the outer world, thereby restricting the ability to react to immediate dangers in the outer environment.

The parasympathetic system restores the body to a more passive and energy-conserving state. It relaxes the body's vital functions, makes the muscles softer, lowers the voice and slows and reduces movement (noticeable particularly when we are tired or very relaxed). When the muscles relax the breathing pattern becomes more open and deeper.

If overpowering impressions do get access to our awareness there is a risk of 'overload.' If the incoming impression

is one of overwhelming physical pain, our awareness simply
shuts down and we become unconscious. When the impression is one of overwhelming psychological pain (trauma), it
can be 'frozen' and encapsulated outside of awareness in the
unconscious. The chemical information packages that
deliver such impressions can be frozen and stored anywhere
in the body, predominantly in the part of the body that was
affected most by the experience.

Brain development and 'psychological problems'

The price *Homo sapiens* has to pay for its advanced brain is
premature birth: that is, the brain has become too big to
permit its full development before birth. Consequently,
unlike most creatures, we are born with a brain that is not
fully developed. In fact we need most of our childhood to
develop the brain's full capacity. If the brain finds itself in an
outer environment that is ideal for its development, the
result is a healthy and harmonious adult person. But if the
environment is not ideal, the body's inner defence mechanisms interfere with and compensate for the environment's
shortcomings as best they can. In other words, we are highly
dependent on our environment in order to develop correctly. So, what are often perceived as psychological problems and disorders can be no more than our inner attempts
to compensate for shortcomings in our development
process.

   Another relevant aspect of the brain's evolution, is that
nature did not design it 'from scratch' as a modern computer engineer would do. It seems to be a basic principle in
evolution that a solution that works is never abandoned. In
other words, development always proceeds through the
modification and expansion of existing structures and functions. The result is that new structures and functions are
added to and have to successfully adapt to those that
evolved previously. Every time the brain has developed and
expanded its abilities, it has done so by adding on new
extensions.

This gradual development of the human brain is easy to observe since it is repeated in the brain development of each individual from foetus to adulthood. As with a building, if we want to build an extension on top of the existing structure, we have to ensure that this is in a solid and stable state. If the oldest parts of the brain fail to develop fully and adequately, the 'newer' parts will be unable to develop and firmly establish themselves. Paul MacLean, now the director of the Laboratory of Brain Evolution and Behaviour in Poolesville, Maryland, has proposed that we actually have a 'triune brain,' that is, a structure of three brains like 'three interconnected biological computers, [each] with its own special intelligence, its own subjectivity, its own sense of time and space and its own memory.' He refers to these three brains as the neocortex or neo-mammalian brain, the limbic or paleo-mammalian system, and the reptilian brain, the brainstem and cerebellum. Each of the three brains is connected to the other two, but each seems to operate as its own system with separate capacities.

The reptilian brain

According to Maclean, the oldest part of the brain is the first to develop in the foetus. It starts to work during the first three months of pregnancy. It is sometimes known as the reptilian brain, since it has remained basically unchanged since the reptilian phase of evolution. This means that the functions of this part of the brain are as limited as the same or equivalent functions as found in reptiles. This level of functionality can be described as the body's 'auto pilot.' It contains the sensory-motor system, spine and nervous system. The functions controlled by this centre are mainly instinctive, genetically determined behaviour. Reptiles are, for example, good at surviving but lack a higher intelligence. This centre also controls the automatic (unconscious) functions which maintain our inner environment at an optimal level. In humans, this part of the brain also handles learnt behaviours such as bike riding, driving a car or typing — once we have acquired such skills to a sufficient level.

The reptilian brain is also good at assessing the environment and adjusting the reactive state accordingly; this is a remnant from the reptilian era when this was essential for survival. These days we have little call for this skill to detect, for example, dangerous animals in our environment. Today we scan our outer world for signals from our social environment (a skill performed very well by businessmen and politicians). We also get assistance from younger parts of the brain in detecting lies and revealing deceitful behaviour, which clearly promotes 'survival' in our social systems. The reptilian brain is also responsible for alerting us to the sudden emergence of crises that require our immediate attention. If the situation is very serious, it has a 'switch' which redirects all the brain's resources to survival mechanisms.

A significant fact about the reptilian brain is that it lacks the ability to distinguish time; everything happens in the present. This plays an important role in how we store memories, in particular from the earliest parts of our lives. Memories from this period may remain stored in our bodies as if they were in some kind of 'time capsule.' A fairly insignificant incident (from an adult point of view but important for the young child) experienced early in life may maintain its intensity throughout life, totally 'unaware' of the lapse of time until it is released and interpreted consciously by the adult mind. The enormous importance and impact which these kinds of incidents can have on adults is well documented in breathwork practice; memories created very early in life, before the brain was fully developed, are often released in this context.

The mammalian brain

When evolution moved on from reptiles to mammals, an expansion of brainpower was required. This led to the first extension of the brain — the limbic system or the emotional/cognitive brain. This is also known as the mammalian brain since the behaviour and functions it controls are shared by all mammals. Smell and hearing are among the functions that are finely controlled by this area of the brain (mammals needed improvement in these areas in order to survive). It also controls our ability to experience emotions and to interpret signals from the world around us, as mammals need better social skills than reptiles.

Another important difference is that reptiles are only aware of the outer world. When evolution reached the mammal stage, this called for increased awareness of the inner world. Unlike the reptilian brain, the mammalian brain can distinguish between present and past time. The mammalian brain is formed between the third and sixth month of pregnancy. This development is visible in small children. At the start, the reptilian brain is dominant. The infant crawls around in a way that has many similarities with reptiles; they are unaware of their inner world and not very good at detecting nuances in the outer world, although they are very good at detecting danger. When the mammalian brain starts to superimpose itself over the reptilian, this leads to a new phase in the child's behaviour. The baby learns to walk, and becomes a toddler with a growing awareness of the outer environment.

This part of the brain is also linked with our ability to handle relationships, both with others and with our body and mind. The mammalian brain also controls the immune system, which could be described as a tool to regulate our relationship with influences in the outer environment that may cause illness. Therapies such as breathwork that facilitate emotion-release can therefore have a direct influence on the immune system.

Neocortex

The next phase in the development of the human brain evolved in order to handle language and the increased thought process that this led to. It also provided the ability to distance oneself emotionally, and to handle situations in a rational rather than instinctual way. All this resulted from the development of the neocortex — the verbal/intellectual brain that only starts to develop during the last three months of pregnancy.

It is this brain extension that started to reveal *Homo sapiens* as different from other mammals, and gave us our unique survival feature. This part of the brain is five times as big as the reptilian and mammalian brains together, and its ability to handle impressions from the outer environment and convert them into creative thoughts is endless.

A highly significant characteristic of the Neocortex is that it can distinguish between past time, present time and future time. In practice this creates our ability to worry, but it also means that we are able to draw conclusions from the past and project them onto questions about the future (What may happen if the same thing that happened yesterday happens again tomorrow?). It also generates our curiosity. The ability to formulate 'What if?' questions is one of the capacities which ensures *Homo sapiens'* current position of dominance in the animal kingdom.

The deciding factor as to whether these tremendous capacities will develop in a positive or negative direction is largely determined during the first three years of our lives, mainly depending on the skill, support and commitment of the people who act as our role-models. It is during this period that we form the foundation for our higher intellect by the development of our emotional functions as a base for continued development.

A positive effect of breathwork is its ability to release memories formed before the brain was fully developed. Making these accessible to the adult brain enables us to use our full brainpower to process and interpret them. Breathwork has shown that once an early 'body memory' (that is, created before the brain was fully developed) has been released, it can be interpreted by the adult brain — even if the impression stored consists only of fragmented impressions of sound, smell, body sensations, and so on, the adult brain can put the pieces together and get the 'full picture.' There are numerous cases in breathwork to confirm this. For example, people have released very detailed memories of birth (people present, what was said etc.) which have then been authenticated by other sources.

The frontal lobes

The frontal part of the brain — the frontal lobes or pre-frontal cortex — does not develop until after birth. This is the youngest part of the brain. It is estimated that it reached its size and function about 40,000 years ago. This is an incredibly short time compared with the several hundred million years it took to develop the oldest parts of the brain.

In eastern cultures this part of the brain is also known as the third eye, and when it is 'opened' it can bring us to a higher level of awareness. In the West it is sometimes known as the silent part. For a long time nobody knew what functions it has, since they were unable to detect any form of activity within it; however today it is regarded as being in charge of higher human qualities such as love, compassion, understanding, and our most advanced intellectual abilities. The frontal lobes have a well-developed contact network with all parts of the brain. It is also the most sensitive part of the brain, and damage here can cause serious problems. Even damage in other parts of the brain may have an impact on the functioning of the frontal lobes.

The development of this part of the brain takes place in two phases. The first phase starts directly after birth and takes place mainly during the first year. How well this development progresses is directly linked with how the parents (or carers) treat the child. The development of the frontal lobes takes place in parallel with the development of other parts of the brain, and is influenced by the outer environment. This means that the frontal lobes develop a very intimate and dynamic link to the older parts of the brain.

The effects that breathwork has on the mind may be related to this close link with the oldest parts, in so far as it effects the frontal lobes by activating the oldest parts of the brain.

During the first six months after birth the brain doubles in size, and by the age of four it has doubled in size once more. At around fifteen years of age, when the other parts of the brain are fully developed and begin to stabilize, the frontal lobes start a second developmental phase that lasts

around six years. Before this phase can be fully imple-
mented, the frontal lobes have to get the other parts of the
brain co-ordinated and synchronized in their functioning.
Only when this has been achieved can the second phase start
in earnest.

There is another noticeable change in the brain's activity
around age fifteen. Prior to this age, the brain's activity level
and oxygen consumption has a metabolism rate equivalent
to that of a marathon runner. But from being twice as high
as in an adult, brain activity suddenly falls to around half its
earlier level and remains at that level for the rest of the individual's life. In the West there is no explanation for this phenomenon, but in the East the assumption is that the body's
inner life energy is active during childhood but withdraws
to a resting position in the root chakra with the onset of
adulthood. The real explanation will probably not be available until we know more about the function of the frontal
lobes, and when we have learnt how to measure 'inner life
energy' scientifically.

The 'fifth' part of the brain

Recent research has changed our view on the link between
the brain and the heart. It is clear that there is a strong neu-
ral network between these organs and that they are in close
contact with each other. More than 60 per cent of the heart
cells have the same form as the nerve cells in the brain. On
the other hand, nerve cells in the heart lack the ability to
process information in the refined way in which the brain
does — the heart can't distinguish the nuances or logic in
incoming information. The heart does not just communicate
with the brain but also with the rest of the body and the
outer world. This communication is undertaken in such a
way that the heart selects the information that corresponds
best with the inner world, and interprets it to fit our individual world view, and this in turn influences how we react.
This communication works both ways. One important
detail is that the impressions from our senses are interpreted
in the brain. This means that what we see, hear, smell and

feel is based on selected information that has been (re)interpreted by the brain in order to fit in with our individual inner world.

The heart in all living beings generates an electromagnetic field (the aura). In an embryo this energy field is developed immediately after conception. Compared to the hearts of other mammals, the human heart generates a strong electromagnetic signal that radiates outwards. The brain too generates electromagnetic signals that can be monitored with an EEG machine. But the signals from the heart are around 50 times stronger than the brain signals. The heart's signals radiate throughout the body and form an electromagnetic field around the whole body (the aura). This field is elliptical and forms a sphere that can reach up to five metres from the body. (It looks a bit like a doughnut with the body in the hole in the middle.) It is strongest at about one metre from the body. The energy field is holographic, that is to say every element contains information representing the whole field.

The frequency of the heart's and the brain's energy fields tend to synchronize, and take the same shape and form. In addition the heart's frequency tends to synchronize with that of other people — a phenomenon strongest between people in close contact, or with whom we have strong relationships (a mother carrying her child in her arms) or other close and open body contact between two people. This means that each heart forms an individual part of the energy field which, collectively, we all form together. At the same time, the heart's close contact and interaction with the brain suggests that each individual person's inner world is reflected to the outside world through this energy field. This is not a new realization — that we all are one and the same, while at the same time we are all unique!

Interaction between the various parts of the brain

The evolutionary process which led to the development of the reptilian brain lasted several hundred million years, and without this solid groundwork the later developments of the human brain would not have been possible. As we have established, all development is made on the principle of utilizing and building on older parts. This means that the oldest parts still carry out the same functions as they always have, in the previous evolutionary phases. The younger parts of the brain bring added sophistication by using and influencing the older parts so that their functions become more adept. You could say that the older parts maintain their integrity while at the same time they get new and increased functions. This works both ways. While it is a brilliant solution to make use of old functions in new forms, it also carries a risk since it means that in some situations it can lead to a conflict about which part of the brain is ultimately in control. These conflicts, which we experience as 'inner' problems, have led us to develop the discipline of psychology to understand and treat them.

Although human beings have the mammalian brain in common with other mammals, it does not function in the same way since the younger parts of the human brain influence the mammalian brain's functions. In order for the younger and more sophisticated parts of the brain to function normally, it is therefore necessary for the older parts to develop and form the proper foundation for these later extensions. If the older parts, in charge of emotions and survival functions, are not developing properly, the younger parts dealing with intellect and logic cannot function properly either. That is to say that the neocortex is unable to integrate its activity with the older parts. In psychological language such a person would find it difficult to make a connection between emotion and thought.

The memory function

As we saw earlier, Stanislav Grof describes memories triggered by breathwork as *a system of condensed experiences* (COEX). He defines this as a dynamic constellation of memories from different periods of the individual's life, with the common denominator of a strong emotional charge of the same quality. This is linked with the way our memories are stored.

Our memory function is handled by the emotional/cognitive mammalian brain which also handles learning. We learn by relating to what we remember from earlier learning. Our more advanced ability to think abstractly (handled by the neocortex) is based on functions in the emotional cognitive brain. Between the reptilian and the mammalian brains there are two important glands. First is the amygdala, which registers our earliest emotional impressions, linked with survival during our first three years of our lives. After this period this function is transferred to the unconscious although it continues to have a predominant influence on how we react in certain situations. The second gland is the hippocampus, which develops from the age of three and handles short-term memory, and the transfer to long term memory.

Both of these glands are mainly focused on survival strategies and relationships to others. When the hippocampus registers what it perceives as 'biologically significant information' (impressions that may have a deep impact on a person and as a consequence may form the base for a COEX system) it sends a message to the brain stem to note and save the impressions and activities in the brain that took place when the information was received. The brain stem registers this and saves it as a 'template' for future impressions. From now on, each time a similar impression is registered, it reinforces the template (like filling in the same lines of a drawing over and over again).

The construction of memory can be compared to a tree. The roots at the bottom consist of our genes — our original individual characteristics which we inherit from our ancestors. The stem consists of the body's information molecules — the chemical information packages that contain thoughts, emotions and physical sensations in chemical form. The branches of our memory tree consist of the thought process, emotions and memories that cooperate to form new information packages delivered to the rest of the body. This process has an impact on how we remember things. Since we constantly register a number of things that take place around us, the brain tries to sort the incoming impressions as best it can. And just like memory artists (whose surprising feats of memory form stage acts or party tricks) we try to anchor each experience in a way that will help us remember them. In the same way most people around the world have very detailed memories of 11 September 2001, while they probably have difficulties remembering what they did on a specific day just a month ago.

Dreams and intuition

Dreams, intuition and creative thinking are activities that are influenced by breathwork, mostly in a positive way. They are all functions handled by the emotional/cognitive mammalian brain which, together with the verbal/intellectual neocortex, can also influence and change functions in the reptilian brain. From around the age of seven our physical reactions are also influenced by abstract thought formed in these two parts of the brain, so that with the help of creative thinking we can influence even the deepest rooted bodily functions. In other words the creative power of our thoughts can influence and reverse even a physical disorder whether it is a common cold or cancer (from which spontaneous recovery is usually seen as a miracle). Another popular example that is used more and more to clearly illustrate our creative brainpower is where through 're-programming' the brain, a person can overcome fear and walk on burning coals.

Compensation for slow development

Nature compensates for the slow development of the brain, by providing help from people in the child's outer environment. During the first five years, before the emotional/cognitive brain is fully functional, the child needs external assistance. For this reason all parents are 're-programmed' to replace the child's missing brain functions. The mother's role is especially significant in the child's early development. She helps the child to establish relationships with other children and adults. She protects the child and makes sure it gets the appropriate care and stimulation to take part in activities that will stimulate a positive development of the child's brain. When the basic structure of the child's brain is developed and operational the mother (or carer) will move on to assist the development of the younger parts of the brain. Since the verbal/intellectual neocortex can't develop until the emotional/cognitive mammalian brain is operational, the mother has to function as the child's neocortex during this period (which means detecting danger, setting an example for the development of language and other intellectual activities, etc.). The father's role is often more peripheral (general protection) at the earliest stages and increases gradually as the child grows up.

Especially during the period immediately after birth, this external assistance is essential. Even minor disturbances can have a negative effect on this development and can disrupt the inner balance. This is often confirmed by the memories triggered in breathwork. In fact the initial incident causing a psychological problem may seem so insignificant, in comparison to its influence on the adult person, that it is difficult to see the connection. A small event such as being trapped in a blanket as a small child may lead to a lifelong feeling of being 'psychologically trapped' in a number of situations. Other common causes of psychological problems detected in breathwork are related to noises, lights and harsh handling during birth.

If the child on the other hand gets adequate external assistance during this initial development in childhood, the brain's later development phases will be less and less dependent on outer assistance.

When the brain is fully developed the emotional part can draw on assistance from both the older and younger parts. This means that a positive emotional state of mind facilitates the thought process by focusing the brain resources in the correct part of the brain. A negative state of mind has the opposite effect and divides the focus, so that the individual parts of the brain start to function as independent units each with a different focus. It is important then for parents to display a positive attitude to life to their child, since it is easier to learn in a positive environment than in a negative one.

The same applies for negative experiences in general. Whether a negative thought or experience, it has the same effect, in that it shifts the focus of the brain from the verbal and intellectual parts to the older survival functions. And regardless of whether the signals come from the verbal/intellectual part or from the sensory-motor function in the reptilian brain, the emotional/cognitive brain will react in the same way. This is why we react in broadly the same way whether we are facing personal criticism, or we are standing face to face with a lion.

Another aspect of the memory function that plays a part in breathwork therapy (and that is also linked with Grof's COEX system of memories) is that memories are not static. Instead, the memory process is creative and constructive, and our memories are constantly changing. We present images from our memory to our consciousness to get its help when we are seeking answers to problems. We constantly analyse and draw conclusions from things we remember, and add new observations to old memories, so that we are constantly reviewing our memories from a new perspective. (Still, when a witness is heard in a court of law, the testimony is often regarded as less reliable if it can't be repeated, virtually word for word, every time.)

Our learning is also linked with different states of mind (known as state-specific learning). What we learn is linked to the mental state we were in when we learnt it. For example, what you learn while you are experiencing fear, is easier to recall on the next occasion you experience fear. This is due to the fact that emotions and learning are handled by the same part of the brain that also controls the immune system and the secretion of hormones. This means that what we learn (the imprints in the brain) is associated with the hormones that were produced by our emotions during the learning experience.

This may play an important role in understanding how breathwork can trigger memories. The increased inner circulation caused by the breathing will help release the chemical messages that contain memories in the form of impressions, thoughts and emotions. The fact that the emotions are given free expression during a breathwork session will help to re-create the mental and emotional state where the initial incident that led to the memory first occurred. This, in turn will allow us to remember even more.

The fact that the brain is divided into sections which control different parts of our behaviour and body-functions limits the healing potential of some forms of therapy available today. To talk about problems (as in counselling) means accessing the neocortex. Therapy which includes more intense emotional catharsis allows access in addition to the cognitive/emotional brain, whereas body therapies and breathwork also provide access to the oldest parts of the brain. Trying to use psychoanalysis to reach the oldest parts of the brain, for instance, can only mean indirect access, since this part of the brain does not deal with language. However, as we have seen earlier, to permanently heal a physical or psychological problem may require just such access to the oldest parts of the brain, in order to change the very roots of a problem.

Since breathwork mainly influences the brain through a change in oxygen intake, this allows access to all parts and functions of the brain. This means that breathwork provides a versatile and powerful tool for healing the body and psyche.

4. *The future of Breathwork*

... our yesterdays are but dreams
our tomorrows merely visions
but today lived well makes
every yesterday a dream of joy
and each tomorrow a vision of promise ...
Sanskrit poem, The Salutation of the Dawn

Having looked at the history of breathwork up to the present day, now it is time to look at its future potential. It is worth stating at the outset that our current knowledge of the power and capacity contained in our own breathing is still based principally on subjective experiences. Still, even the very limited research in this field has confirmed that the traditional knowledge is remarkably precise, given how it has been obtained. With the technical resources we have today, and those we will have in the future, it is very likely that we will get a much better understanding of the breath, and that we will develop ways of utilizing this incredibly flexible and versatile tool, both for our physical and mental wellbeing, as well as for expanding our latent physical and mental resources.

As we have seen, the breath has a central role in the body. It can help us to maintain our health, and to provide the body with the best possible working conditions; and it can help to restore our health when we fall ill. With the right approach, breathing is safe, inexpensive and completely without side-effects. At the moment, the greatest obstacle is ignorance rather than an unwillingness to try something new. But if nothing else, one positive effect of the growing crisis in the health care sector may be that it will force us to consider cheaper alternatives. This may provide the vital opportunity for breathwork.

Breathwork has already begun to contribute to western psychology by opening up a new East/western integration that removes the barriers between psychology and religion, and which has a wider interpretation of consciousness. This is a necessary phase if we are to continue to develop and expand our consciousness beyond known borders with the help of psychology.

In order to prevent the increasing effects of globalization from being completely dominated by financial interests and exploitation of each other's resources, we need to increase our understanding and respect for different cultures. When it is possible physically to reach almost any part of the planet, and when a message can reach all corners of the world virtually instantaneously, people can no longer claim to be isolated from others. To survive, we need to cooperate. To maintain the illusion that the western world will be able to continue to live in abundance, when other parts of the world struggle for survival, simply demonstrates a lack of vision and clarity. What is needed is for the whole planet to function as a single unit rather than as discrete nations or continents.

It may seem extreme (especially with the current number of threats of conflict in many parts of the world) to suggest that breathwork may help to unite nations and cultures. But if we look at the largest peaceful gathering this planet sees — the Olympic Games — it is easy to see the importance of rituals (fire, flag, opening and closing ceremonies, and so on). When people who lack common language and culture meet it helps to find things we have in common that go beyond the differences. In smaller groups, shared breathwork sessions are known to have such an effect.

Breathwork and politics

The political system in most western countries usually consists of a left and a right wing; that is, a liberal and conservative approach respectively. Regardless of how this division is made (right/left, republican/democrat, conservative/liberal or labour) they are based on different basic views.

According to the left wing it is the environment that needs changing if we are to improve the world. Their resources are focused on improving the outer environment, assuming that we all react the same way to change in this area. Our inner world has no place in this philosophy. If a person has (for example) difficulties in finding a job, the explanation lies in the capitalistic world order that impacts on us all equally.

But according to the right wing, the situation is really the reverse. They see our 'inner environment' as the essential part that needs to be improved when things go wrong. If a person is unemployed, that is not the fault of society; rather it is down to each individual to get themselves together and be more willing to do what it takes to get a job. This dualistic approach to life is based on the same worldview that forms the basis for modern western science which divides the world into an inner and outer aspect. Ken Wilber calls this 'flatland' since it deals with a single dimension of human behaviour.[65]

Even if this is a very crude image of the western world, it is evident that these different approaches still play a dominant role in politics. Still the clear road to a better future is to consider both inner and outer environments, in tandem. This does not just apply to the political world, but rather to the overall view that separates our inner and outer worlds.

Ken Wilber's solution is an integrated transformative view. To achieve this he has formed an ITP network (ITP — Integral Transformative Practice) with the aim of encouraging people worldwide to change their lives, based on a view that considers both the individual inner and outer world and the society we live in. On the individual level this means becoming aware of nutrition, exercise, and other ways of taking care of our body, but also to try to get a deeper meaning in life with the help of meditation, breathing techniques, religion, psychotherapy and similar. It may mean a deeper involvement in order to help others, to become active politically or in environmental issues, but also to make use of the social situation and get help from family and friends to further our personal development.

For a devout physicist like me
the difference between past, present and future
is just a stubborn illusion.

Albert Einstein

Breathwork and the environment

One of the key issues for the future is our approach to nature. In order to achieve real and sustainable change to our current destructive way of life, Michel Odent argues that we need to go right back to where we started and make sure future generations get the best possible start in life. Only when we can do this can we start to hope for a change in our destructive behaviour.

We already know enough, for example, to realize that our current western convention that women are better off giving birth in hospital has its obvious problems. But in order to make a change, it requires a wider understanding of exactly what damage an incorrect start in life can cause. This may be one of the areas where breathwork can play an important role, since it is one of very few techniques that allow us access to memories from our own birth. Not until a person has re-experienced the pain they may have experienced at birth, will they be able to fully understand how badly some babies are handled in the hospital environment (albeit with the best of intentions.)

The really positive aspect of breathwork however is that it does not just make it possible to explore our unconscious mind, it also heals inner wounds and sets right what has been done wrong. My personal vision for the future is that it will be as natural for all of us to have a breath 'workout' as it is to workout physically today, and that future generations will find it obvious and natural to do regular breathing exercises along with mental and physical relaxation, as it is today to give the muscles regular exercise.

Study the past if you want to foresee the future.

Confucius

Breathwork and education

If breathwork were introduced as a theoretical and practical subject at school it would probably have a positive effect not just on the contact between students, but also on their ability to learn. There is much evidence that confirms that learning is more difficult in stressful environments. To shut out negative impressions, at the same time as we try to take in the positive, just doesn't work. More likely in these circumstances is that the brain shifts from its cognitive functions to those dealing with survival.

The school environment is also our first socialization process. It does not matter how much parents and teachers distance themselves from this environment, they still play a part in what takes place there. One reason is that children are more sensitive to emotions and demands from their environment, and better than adults at acting them out. Instead of denying this, there is much that older generations can learn from observing children. For example, children learn what they see adults do, more quickly than from what they are *told* to do. Our need to fit in socially is deeply rooted in our original pack behaviour. In order to understand and change this, it may be necessary to reach deep inside ourselves and get in touch with our most basic needs. Breathwork can do this.

Wage peace with your breath
Breathe in firemen and rubble,
Breathe out whole buildings
And flocks of redwing blackbirds.
Breathe in terrorists and breathe out sleeping children
And freshly mown fields.
Breathe in confusion and breathe out maple trees.
Breathe in the fallen
And breathe out lifelong friendships intact.

Mary Oliver

Breathwork and peace efforts

Breathwork is a way of bringing people together in a way that reaches far beyond mere social contact. If all important meetings between our world leaders started with some form of ritual involving breathwork, our planet would probably not be as full of conflict as it is today. This may sound like a flimsy New Age idea, but to get together both spiritually and mentally at important gatherings is a tradition with deep roots. Even if the religious rituals in our modern western world lack a deeper significance for many of us, most countries still use religious rituals at a number of important occasions in a person's life.

Another vital aspect of our social lives is how we handle conflicts. Between us we possess an enormous fund of knowledge, and we can access wisdom enough to bring about radical changes in society. But this does not prevent us from being involved in constant conflicts, about nations, race, creed, money, pride, power, and so on. During the hippie era, the phrase *Make Love Not War* was coined. This was very much the result of large groups in society that started to open up their minds and have transpersonal experiences, leading to an unprecedented wave of radical change in large parts of the western world. Suddenly it was more important to reach agreements than actually to be right about something. We started to look for deeper relationships, both with each other and with nature and our individual roots.

As Stanislav Grof was able to establish, drugs were not the all-important ingredient in this transition. As he points out, all it really takes is for us to learn to use our own breathing in order to reach a higher state of consciousness. This is good news, since we also learnt from the hippie era that drugs have a very negative side.

According to Chinese thinking, yin energy leads to a point where it is so strong that it spontaneously turns into yang energy. In mathematics there are similar rules that state that too much order leads to chaos, and chaos over a certain degree leads to order. In many western countries there is a clear focus on achieving as much order as possible. But despite the obvious positive effects this has on our societies, it is almost impossible to achieve. Several countries have tried different methods, but as soon as people feel the presence of 'too much' order, it tends to have a negative effect. If the attempts are perceived as controlling, it may lead to covert activities by dissidents, while on the individual level the reaction may be destructive behaviour in the form of alcohol abuse and so on. But it can also lead to positive reactions where people try to create activities to spontaneously lighten up the situation. This may be in the form of celebrations, very often after the country has won a victory in sports.

The approach that body and mind are separate and beyond our reach does not make things better. We need rest as well as activity, leisure time as well as work. To pause for rest and restoration of our inner peace at regular intervals, or on a daily basis, is something that many would like to achieve, but far fewer actually attempt. It demands that we really allow ourselves time off from the material world in order to take care of our inner selves. As obvious as it is that we need balance to our daily work, we also need to balance the stress created simply by living, for example, in a modern city. Breathwork and meditation are by far the most cost-efficient way, both for society and nature, to achieve this.

So rather than trying to achieve too much order in society, our goal should be to achieve balance. To find ways of allowing space for all our human needs; both for order, but also for chaos, both as societies and as individuals.

Formerly, religion played a part and demanded respect for the different use of weekdays and Sundays. Work was for weekdays, worship for weekends. Religious holidays were also respected in a different way, and in part this was to give structure, rhythm and balance week by week, and season by season. For various reasons much of this has disappeared from today's societies. One reason is the weakened position of the established churches; another is the materialistic western worldview that has led us away from our inner world to the outer materialistic world.

And this inner world is another area where breathwork can play a role in helping us get in touch with ourselves, our individual history as well as our common history. The sense of a deeper contact with our inner self does not just increase the understanding of ourselves, it also unites us with our relatives as well as our fellow human beings. At the same time as bringing us in touch with our common archetypes, we get a clearer understanding of our common symbolic language as well as the importance of marking the various seasons, our relationship to nature and our inner qualities.

After the creative forces retreat, they return. In human affairs those of like mind and character join harmoniously together in new undertakings. This mirrors the movement of the Tao. There is movement but not brought about by force. The movement is natural, arising spontaneously. For this reason the transformation of the old becomes easy. The old is discarded and the new introduced. Both measures accord with the time; therefore no harm results.

I Ching

Breathwork and drug abuse

There is one aspect of drug abuse where breathwork can play a role. In particular the western world is threatened by the ever more widespread use of drugs — a form of abuse that spreads to ever younger children. The debate that this provokes is usually around which preventive method is most effective. Should we go for punishment or treatment? Should we blame parents, authorities, schools or perhaps pop idols who set a bad example? These are extremely important questions since drug abuse often leads to severe problems, not just for the abuser but also for society as a whole. But although the discussion covers most possible aspects, it generally misses the possible link between such abuse and the almost systematic 'cultural cleansing' of anything that may bring a deeper meaning to the children's situation — despite the overt search for alternative realities that we see in many children and teenagers (and may be a contributing factor to the popularity of books and films including *Harry Potter*, and *The Lord of the Rings)*.

Parents learn very quickly that children love to experience different realities, whether in the form of fairy stories, films, computer games, or amusement parks. Curiosity is a strong driving force in human beings. What we call superstition (believing that there are other realities beyond everyday reality, with spirits and higher forces) and treat rather dismissively today was once a reality throughout life.

But one consequence of our modern materialistic worldview (strongly supported by science) is that our alternative realities have disappeared. Phenomena that had a great impact on people through folklore — but which could not be proven with cold, objective facts— were dismissed as superstition and nonsense. Even our churches (albeit acting as representatives of faith) have done their best to bring in a more materialistic worldview. Our schools have followed in their footsteps and changed their teaching of religion, from a spiritual path to be experienced as a possible route to a deeper and more meaningful life, to an abstract subject to be observed and studied.

Together this has led to a general demystification of life for our children. Life is what you see and experience in your everyday reality, no more and no less. At the same time, and at many schools, drugs are freely available and may introduce completely new worlds and realities. For many children drugs are not even a new phenomenon; many of them are second generation users. It does not take much to understand how temptation can outweigh the perceived risks.

Another important development that affects today's children is that their environment has become a much safer place, in many ways, and this is something parents and society have worked hard to achieve. But while it is important to provide a safe play area for children, it is also important to accept that human nature demands a certain amount of stimulus to develop properly. To test one's own ability and one's limits is important for all children; to experience fear close by gives a sense of courage: to know that we are courageous makes us feel good. All children have a need to explore and test the world. Of course this is not to say that we should make their play areas more dangerous, but instead of supplying them with surrogate experiences to compensate for their lack of real experiences (as we do eagerly today in the form of violent films, computer games and toys) we should consider supplying them with other opportunities. It is mainly a question of seeing our children's world differently, but it can also mean direct actions.

One such action could be to re-introduce initiations to our children's lives. It is only a few generations ago that most children became adults over night when they were confirmed as full members of their church, able to receive the Holy Sacraments alongside their parents and other adult members. It was a clear signal that helped children to step out of their world and into the adult world. Today there are still plenty of initiations around, but unfortunately they are mainly in the form of dangerous games, drugs or behaviour, out of reach and beyond the control of adults. An alternative to this, that — although it is safe — may give sufficiently intense experiences to have an impact, is breathwork and meditation.

Always aim at complete harmony
  of thought and word and deed.
Always aim at purifying your thoughts
  and everything will be well.

Mahatma Gandhi

'Sacred Contracts'

Caroline Myss argues that all human beings have a higher purpose in life.[66] By this she means that, before we are born, our higher self has set up a kind of goal for what we would like to achieve in life. It can be compared with the eastern law of karma that says that what we have done in previous lives will affect us in this life. According to Myss this higher goal is so important to us that she calls it 'a sacred contract.' It is so important to us that when we don't live in a way that will lead us to this goal, it may make us ill both physically and mentally. And — the other side of the coin — if we can identify our goal, our sacred contract, this may have a very positive influence on our lives.

Whether or not we accept Myss' theory in full, there is an element of truth in it that most of us can subscribe to: when a person feels that they are in the 'right' place, with the 'right' people, doing the 'right' thing, this gives a positive outlook on life that has a huge impact on that person's life. We jokingly say that people in love seldom get sick. If somebody tried to prove this statistically it would probably be true.

To find our true place and task in this life calls for some deep soul searching. It requires a certain self-knowledge, that we know our deeper thoughts and motives as well as the more superficial. Here too, breathwork is a uniquely versatile tool. If we all used breathwork to find our true place and role in life, and as a consequence experienced greater personal satisfaction, this would be an enormous saving for society.

Statistics show that a large proportion of the medical

resources in the West are spent on people who aren't really in need of medical care. Rather, they are looking for ways to sort out their lives, which they characterize as unsatisfactory or wrong, but don't know how to get back on track. To identify physical symptoms for this, and to prescribe medicine may be a short-term solution, but statistics show that this situation is repeated and continued in a way that is not useful for either patient or health care, since modern medicine is not really equipped to deal with this kind of life-support and guidance.

One attempt to resolve this problem is a new theory of health, developed in Sweden, known as KASAM (a Swedish anagram which means having a *feeling of context and meaning* in life). It has many similarities with the theory of sacred contracts. The feeling of context is linked with every aspect of a person's life and the result of the interaction between a person and their environment. The KASAM theory has three main elements. The first is the importance of being able to explain and understand what happens in life. The second is to be able to manage this — that we don't feel victims of uncontrollable circumstances, but have the means to affect them. The third element is to feel that life is meaningful — that we are part of the processes that form our everyday life.

A yuga is the time needed for an angel to come down from heaven, once a year, to sweep her wing over the top of a high mountain and thus wear it down to the ground.

Indian sutra

Breathwork and the New Age

There are still many in the West who regard breathwork as 'New Age nonsense.' Such people would say that to manipulate the breath has no scientific backing and is a rather pointless activity. But as we have seen, breathing techniques are as old as human history. To regard breathwork as new and unscientific is therefore more a sign of western arrogance, displayed by certain physicians, scientists and also by many religious groups as well as authorities.

The expression New Age may also require an explanation. The expression originates from the eastern view that the world is divided into eras *(yugas)*. Each era reflects humankind's spiritual level, reaching from the darkest age, where people live solely in the material world, to the lightest, where humankind has reached its highest level of awareness with advanced spiritual development. Our present era is called *Kali Yuga* (after the Indian goddess Kali, who swallowed the evil in order to make room for the good). Yugas too are divided in shorter periods and the period at the end of Kali Yuga is known as the New Age. This New Age refers to the dawning of a new era with a higher awareness.

A common misconception (perhaps mainly from critics) is that the so-called New Age movement started with the 1960s' and 1970s' hippie movement. Certainly the name itself started to spread during this time, and one reason was the musical *Hair* where they sang about 'the dawning of the age of Aquarius.' But the views usually ascribed to New Age are much older, with roots in the eighteenth century Romantic period. Many ideas were added during the following two centuries. In any case, the New Age ideology is vague and varies from person to person or group to group, and even from country to country. The only clear common denominator is that it is not a specific religion or even a shared opinion. Wouter Hanegraaf has studied the New Age movement in detail. According to him some of the characteristics of New Age are:

Believing that 'thought is creative.' That is to say that all we experience is relative and differs from person to person.
Believing in a holistic worldview. That all in the universe is interlinked.
Believing in a higher meaning behind the development of our universe. That nothing happens randomly.

Psychologizing religion and sacralization of psychology.
That the borders between psychology and religion are gradually being removed. This is mainly a consequence of transpersonal experiences that has formed new schools in psychology.

Believing in a new world order. That the world is heading for a new phase — such beliefs ranging from more realistic aspects to believing that paradise is around the corner.[67]

None of these views is unique to the New Age movement, and many aspects are reflected, as we have seen, in new scientific insights into a dynamic and interconnected universe. The more negative image for many, however, comes from some extreme views and activities that we associate with New Age. These have led to the image of a worldview dominated by too much faith in intuition, misinterpretation of deeper truths by people not ready for them and unwilling to adhere to them properly, mixed with unwillingness to accept and believe theoretical knowledge.

One such expression is that many New Age followers prefer to see themselves as a 'medium' channelling information from higher sources rather than expressing it as their own views. This phenomenon is often reflected in New Age literature *(The Celestine Prophecy* being one of the more successful). According to Hanegraaf one of the most influential New Age writers is Shirley MacLean. Without commenting on her literary skills, it is questionable if she intended to achieve this position when she wrote her light-hearted stories about her personal mystical experiences.

Another successful author who deliberately set out to balance this New Age approach to knowledge is the Norwegian philosophy teacher Jorstein Gaarder. In his equally popular book *Sophie's World* he attacks what he sees as the lack of respect for ancient knowledge from New Age groups. After a thorough presentation of the thoughts and theories that have formed the western world, he concludes that it is wrong to dismiss the whole of western culture, simply because some of us are too ignorant of our history to think that we know better. An interesting observation is that the book is written in a way that addresses young children.

A further criticism against New Age is that it is characterised by immature people who don't want to grow up and take their part in wider social responsibility. Even if this is exaggerated, there may be an element of truth in it. One reason for this may be that transpersonal experiences often bring the individual in touch with archetypes that are difficult to face and accept, in particular when they reflect the darker sides of human behaviour. One of the easiest archetypes to accept is that of the inner child. It has in fact become so popular to try to get in touch with our inner child that many equate this with New Age courses. But however important it is to re-establish contact with our inner child, this is only one step on the path to a higher level of awareness. And for our planet as a whole, it needs more from the species that currently poses the greatest threat to it, than to become like happy children in adult bodies.

We also need to learn to handle initiative, leadership, power, compassion, fairness, organizational skills and so on. The list is long. There is a long way to go yet, if we are to get a better world. But to criticize and dismiss new ways and ideas completely is not very helpful. Nor does it help to focus all resources on being 'anti' rather than 'for' society (another New Age hallmark). To work together within our societies to achieve goals is usually a better option. But regardless if we are for or against New Age, and regardless of how we choose to categorize breathwork, one thing is certain: to utilize the power and capacity of our own breath is something that will be with us for the rest of human history, as it has ever been.

Endnotes

1 Lowen, 1990 pp.37–38
2 Speads, 1992, p.41
3 Garfield, 1977
4 Fried, 1990
5 Speads, 1978
6 Swami Rana, 1998
7 Recommended by Ilse Middendorf, founder of Ilse Middendorfs Institute in Berlin
8 Dr Harold Katz, founder of The California Breath Clinics
9 Fried, 1990
10 Speads, 1992
11 Wilhelm, 1962 pp.21–22
12 Zang 1985
13 Sanella, 1978, p.1
14 Neil Douglas-Klotz 1995
15 *Vigiliae Christianae* 2001
16 *de Dacia*, 1965. Author's translation
17 Sanella, 1976, p.14
18 Main, *Kalahari*, 1987
19 Bjerre, 1960
20 Eliade, 1967
21 Staunton, 2002, italics in original
22 In Staunton, *2002*
23 Minett, 1994, p.50–51
24 Minett, 1994, p.55
25 *Ibid*
26 Minett, 1994, p.52
27 Wahlström, 2003
28 Ray and Orr, 1977
29 Minett, 1994, p.50–51
30 Staunton, *2002, p.2*
31 Chamberlain, 1996
32 Michel Odent 1994
33 Chamberlain, 1998
34 Rachana, 2000
35 Odent, 1994
36 *Ibid*
37 Grof, 1985 p.97
38 Ring, 2000, p.19.
39 Ring, 2000, p.26
40 Fenwick, 1995
41 Grof, 1998, pp.5–6
42 Grof 1998, p.6
43 Grof, 1998
44 John Welwood 2000
45 Welwood, 2000, pp.4–5
46 Lewis, 1997
47 Fried, 1990 p. 59
48 Fried 1990
49 *Ibid*
50 Bradley, 1991
51 Grof, 2000, p.185
52 Grof, 2000, p.192
53 Grof, 2000, p.193
54 Robert B. Livingston 1992
55 Livingston, 1992
56 Pert 1997
57 Harner 1980
58 Achterberg, 2002
59 Thomas Kuhn 1962
60 Ellison, 2002, p.20
61 Myss 1996
62 Achterberg 2002
63 Myss 1996
64 Barbro Lindström, 1987
65 Ken Wilber 2000
66 Myss 2001
67 Hanegraaf 1996

Bibliography

Achterberg, Jeanne. *Imagery in Healing, Shamanism and Modern Medicine*. Boston, USA: Shambhala, 2002.

Albery, Nicolas. *How to Feel Reborn?* London: Regeneration Press, 1985.

Benson, Herbert, Stark Marg. *Timeless Healing, The Power and Biology of Belief*. New York: Simon/Schuster, 1997.

Berendt, Joachim-Ernst. *Nada Brahma: The World is Sound*. Rochester, Vermont: Destiny Books, 1987.

Bjerre, Jens. Kalahari, London UK: Michael Joseph, 1960.

Bloom, William. *The Endorphin Effect*. London, UK: Piatkus, 2001.

Bradley, Dinah. *Hyper Ventilation Syndrome, A Handbook for Bad Breathers*.New Zealand: Tandem Press, 1991.

Burnett Taylor, Edward. *Religion in Primitive Culture*. New York: Harper Torchbook, 1958.

Chamberlain, David. *The Mind of Your Newborn Baby*. Berkeley, California: North Atlantic Books, 1996.

Chilton Pearce, Joseph. *The Biology of Transcendence, A Blueprint of the Human Spirit*. Rochester, Vermont, USA: Park Street Press, 2002.

Clarke, Isabel, ed. *Psychosis and Spirituality*. London, UK: Whurr Publishers, 2001.

de Dacia, Petrus. *Om den saliga jungfrun Kristina av Stommeln*. Stockholm: Bonniers, 1965.

Douglas-Klotz, Neil. *Desert Wisdom, The Middle Eastern Tradition — from the Goddess to the Sufis*. London, UK: Thorsons, 1995.

Ehrmann, Wilfried. *Handbuch der Atemtherapie*. Austria: Param-Verlag, 2004.

Ellison, Arthur J. *Science and the Paranormal, Altered States of Reality*. UK: Floris Books, 2002.

Fenwick, Peter, & Fenwick, Elisabeth. *The Truth in the Light*. New York: Berkeley Books, 1995.

Fried, Robert. *The Breath Connection*. New York: Insight Books, 1990.

—, *Breathe Well, Be Well*. New York: John Wiley & Son, Inc, 1999.

Govinda, Lama Anagarika. *Foundations of Tibetan Mysticism*. London: Rider & Co, 1960.

Grof, Stanislav. *Realms of the Human Unconscious*, New York: Viking Press, 1975.

—, (1988) *The Adventure of Self-Discovery*. Albany: State University of New York Press, 1988.

—, & Grof, Christina. *The stormy search for the self*. Los Angeles CA: Mandala, 1989.

234 ⇔ *Exhale: An Overview of Breathwork*

—, *The Thirst for Wholeness, Attachment, Addiction and the Spiritual Path*. San Francisco, USA: Harper San Francisco, 1993.

—, *The Cosmic Game, Explorations of the Frontiers of Human Consciousness*. Albany, USA: State University of New York Press, 1998.

—, *Psychology of the Future, lessons from modern consciousness research*. Albany, USA: State University of New York Press, 2000.

Hanegraaf, Wouter J. *New Age Religion and Western Culture, Esotericism in the Mirror of Secular Thought*. New York: E. J. Brill, 1996.

Haraldsson, Erlendur *Studies in Alternative Therapies*. Copenhagen: INRAT, 1994.

Harner, Michael *The Way of the Shaman*. San Francisco: Harper & Row, 1980.

Jacobson, B & Eklund G, *et al. Perinatal origin of adult self destructive behaviour*. Sweden: ACTA Psychiatr. Scand., 76:364–371, 1987.

Jacobson, B & Bygdemon, M. *Obstetric care and proneness of offspring to suicide as adults: case-control study*. London, UK: British Medical Journal, 317, 1346–49, 1998.

Jankhe, Roger. *The Healing Promise of Qi, Creating Extraordinary Wellness Through Qigong and Tai Chi*. USA: Contemporary Books, 2002.

Johari, Harish. *Chakras: Energy Centers of Transformation*. Vermont: Destiny Books, 1987.

Kent, Howard. *Breathe better Feel Better*. London, UK: Apple Press, 1997.

Khalsa, Guru Dharam Singh & O´Keefe, Darryl. *Kundalini, The Essence of Yoga*. London, UK: Gaia Books, 2002.

Kuhn, Thomas. *The nature of scientific revolutions*. Chicago: Chicago UP, 1962.

Lewis, Dennis. *The Tao of Natural Breathing*. California, USA: Mountain Wind Publishing, 1997.

Livingston, Robert B. *Gentle Bridges, Conversations with the Dalai Lama on the Sciences of the Mind*. Boston, USA: Shambhala, 1992.

Lowen, Alexander. *The Spirituality of the Body: Bioenergetics for Grace and Harmony*. New York: Macmillan, 1990.

Lowen, Alexander. *The Language of the Body*. New York: Collier Books, 1958.

Magarian, Gregory J. *Hyperventilation Syndromes*. USA: The Williams & Wilkins Co, 1982.

Middendorf, Ilse. *The Perceptible Breath, Paderborn*. Germany: Junfermann, 1990.

Minett, Gunnel. *Breath and Spirit: Rebirthing as a Healing Technique*. UK: Aquarius, 1994.

Myss, Caroline. *Anatomy of the Spirit, The Seven Stages of Power and Healing*. London, UK: Bantam Books, 1996.

—, *Sacred Contracts, Awakening Your Divine Potential*. New York: Harmony Books, 2001.

Odent, Michel. *Primal Health, A Blueprint for Our Survival*. London, UK: Century, 1986.

—, 'Birth and Rebirth of Culture,' lecture from Science and Mysticism conference on Birth and Rebirth. Middlesex, England: The Scientific & Medical Network, 1994.

Pearsall. Paul. *The Heart's Code*. London: HarperCollins, 1998.

Pert, Candace B. *Molecules of Emotion, Why You Feel the Way You Feel*. New York: Simon & Schuster, 1997.

Rachana, Shivam. *Lotus Birth*. Steels Creek, Australia: Greenwood Press, 2000.

Ring, Kenneth & Elsaesser Valarino, Evelyn. *Lessons from the Light, What we can learn from the near-death experience*. Portsmouth, USA: Moment Point Press, 2000.

Rossi, Ernest Lawrence. *The Psychobiology of Mind-Body Healing, New Concepts of Therapeutic Hypnosis*. New York: Norton & Company, 1993.

Sanella, Leo. *Kundalini: Psychosis or Transcendence?* San Francisco: H.S. Dakin Co, 1977.

Sheldrake, Rupert, McKenna, Terence & Abraham, Ralph. *Chaos Creativity and Cosmic Consciousness*. Vermont, USA: Park Street Press, 2001.

Speads, Carola. *Ways to Better Breathing*. Rochester Vermont, USA: Healing Arts Press, 1992.

Staunton, Tree, ed. *Body Psychotherapy*. Hove, East Sussex, UK: Brunner-Routledge, 2002.

Swami Rama, Ballentine, Rudolph & Hymes, Alan. *Science of Breath, A Practical Guide*. Honsdale, PA. USA: The Himalayan Institute Press, 1998.

Tart, Charles. Contribution to Beyond the Brain Conference. Cambridge, England, 1998.

Taylor, Kylea. *The Ethics of Caring, Honoring the Web of Life in Our Professional Healing Relationship*. Santa Cruz, CA: Hanford Mead Publishers, 1994.

Timmons, Beverly H. & Ley, Ronald, eds. *Behavioral and Psychological Approaches to Breathing Disorders*. New York: Plenum Press, 1994.

Vitebsky, Piers. *The Shaman*. London: Duncan Baird Publishers, 2001.

Van Lysebeth, Andre. *Pranayama, the Yoga of Breathing*. London: Unwin Paperbacks, 1979.

Weller, Stella *The Breath Book*. London, UK: Thorsons, 1999.

Welwood, John. *Toward a Psychology of Awakening*. London: Shambhala, 2002.

Wilber, Ken. *A Theory of Everything*. Boston: Shambhala, 2001.

—, *The Eye of Spirit*. Boston: Shambhala, 2001.

Wilhelm, Richard. *The Secret of the Golden Flower*. New York: Harvest/HBJ Books, 1962.

Zang, Ming wu Sun Xingyuan. *Chinese Qigong therapy*. Jinan, China: Shandong Science and Technology Press, 1985.

Resources

Breathwork is not something that can be learnt from books alone. In order to fully appreciate its results it is necessary to get instructions from a qualified teacher. Below is a list of some sources where it is possible to find schools and training centres for the various techniques mentioned in this book. The list is far from comprehensive, and this is a fast growing area, so the intention is rather to point in the right direction as a starting point for further search on the local level.

Yoga These days it is possible to find yoga schools in almost every town and city throughout the world. Please note however that not all yoga schools have the same focus on breathing exercises.

Tai Chi This is another technique that is easily found in most places around the world. Here too there is a great variety of ways it is taught, so make sure to find the variation that suits you best.

Authentic Breathing News is a web-based, e-mail newsletter that includes insights and practices for natural, authentic breathing from Dennis Lewis, author of *Free Your Breath, Free Your Life*, as well as recent breath-related research. For more information go to *www.authentic-breathing.com*

International Breathwork Foundation This is an international breathwork organization with local representatives in a number of countries. The network is open to all interested in breathwork. Their website is *www.ibfnetwork.org*. It is the best source of information about Rebirthing practitioners worldwide. Please note that qualifications and trainings may vary from country to country.

International Breathwork Training Alliance. www.breath-

workalliance.org is an alliance of breathwork schools, trainers and practitioners worldwide who agree upon published ethics and principles for the practice of breathwork. It also includes schools and training programmes that abide by published standards for their training of breathworkers as well as schools who agree to an exchange of trainers and students in their programmes. Email: jim@transformationsusa.com and awakening@essence.org.

Leonard Orr For more information about Leonard Orr go to *www.rebirthingbreathwork.com*

Transformations Incorporated is the umbrella organization for The School of Spiritual Psychology offering a three year certificate or academic degrees for self-transformation and healing and the Transformations Breathwork Training Program offering four levels of certification as a breathwork practitioner. Their website is: *www.transformationsusa.com*

Holotropic Breathwork To get more information about Holotropic Breathwork please go to *www.breathwork.com*. This is the official website for the Association for Holotropic Breathwork International. AHBI encourages membership networking, personal and professional growth, research, public participation, continuing education, and high ethical standards to improve and preserve Holotropic Breathwork. Membership includes subscription to the quarterly newsletter, *The Inner Door*. Email: info@breathwork.com. Tel: 1-520-760-2335 Fax 520-760-7446.

Stanislav Grof For more information about Grof Transpersonal Training go to *www.holotropic.com*

Birth related issues For more information about Michel Odent and the Primal Health Research Data Bank go to *www.birthworks.org/primalhealth*. For more information about the Association for Pre- & Perinatal Psychology and Health go to *www.birthpsychology.com*.

Index